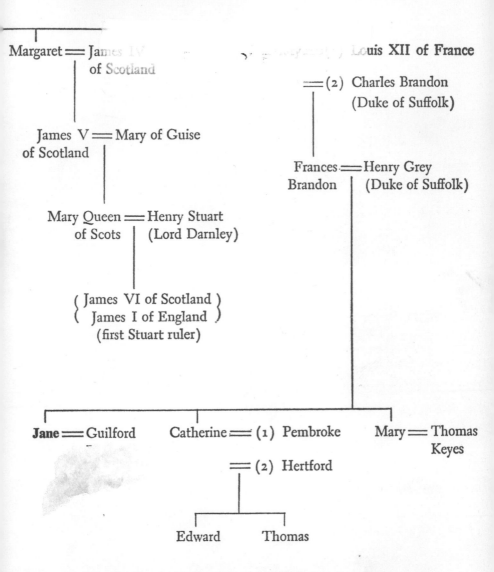

Margaret ══ James IV
of Scotland

Louis XII of France

══ (2) Charles Brandon
(Duke of Suffolk)

James V ══ Mary of Guise
of Scotland

Frances ══ Henry Grey
Brandon (Duke of Suffolk)

Mary Queen ══ Henry Stuart
of Scots (Lord Darnley)

(James VI of Scotland)
(James I of England)
(first Stuart ruler)

Jane ══ Guilford   Catherine ══ (1) Pembroke   Mary ══ Thomas
Keyes

══ (2) Hertford

Edward   Thomas

❧ *The World of Lady Jane Grey* ❧

IANA GRAYA

Regia stirps tristi cinxi diademate crines
Regna sed omnipotens hinc meliora dedit

LADY JANE GREY

(A royal offspring, I bound my locks with a sad diadem
But God gave me better kingdoms thereafter)

From *Herωologia Anglica* by Henry Holland; London, 1620

The world of

Lady Jane Grey

❈   ❈   ❈   ❈   ❈

Gladys Malvern

❈   ❈   ❈   ❈

The Vanguard Press, Inc. ❈ New York

Contents

Three Royal Ladies ❋ 9

Catherine ❋ 23

The King's House ❋ 35

Death of a Tyrant ❋ 46

The Seymours ❋ 57

Chelsea Manor ❋ 73

The Greatest Grief ❋ 82

Northumberland ❋ 94

The Warning ❋ 111

Edward ❋ 118

The Mysterious Summons ❋ 128

Long Live the Queen! ❋ 141

Mary ❋ 150

February 12, 1554 ❋ 166

Epilogue ❋ 183

A Note About Names ❋ 186

List of Illustrations

frontispiece

Lady Jane Grey. From *Herwologia Anglica* by Henry Holland; London, 1620. Courtesy of The New York Public Library, Rare Book Room

following p. 48

Henry VIII: Hans Holbein. Corsini Gallery, Rome. Alinari-Art Reference Bureau

Henry VIII and his family: Princess Mary, Edward, the Queen, and Princess Elizabeth: Unknown artist. Hampton Court. Copyright Reserved

following p. 64

Group at Henry VIII's deathbed: Unknown artist. By courtesy of The National Portrait Gallery, London

Charles Brandon, Duke of Suffolk, Jane Grey's grandfather: Unknown artist. By courtesy of The National Portrait Gallery, London

Edward Seymour, Duke of Somerset, uncle and Protector of Edward VI: Unknown artist. By courtesy of The National Portrait Gallery, London

Thomas Seymour, Baron Seymour of Sudeley, uncle of Edward VI: Unknown artist. Courtesy of The National Maritime Museum, Greenwich, England *following p. 80*

Jane Seymour, mother of Edward VI: Hans Holbein. Windsor Castle. Reproduced by gracious permission of Her Majesty Queen Elizabeth II

Edward VI: Unknown artist. Windsor Castle. Copyright Reserved

Edward VI: Hans Holbein. The Metropolitan Museum of Art, New York, The Jules S. Bache Collection, 1949

John Dudley, Duke of Northumberland: Unknown artist. Reproduced by permission of the Rt. Hon. Viscount De L'Isle, V.C., from his collection at Penshurst Place, Kent

following p. 96

Newhall Castle (later called Beaulieu), one of Princess Mary's residences. From *Palaces and Progresses of Elizabeth*, by Ian Dunlop. Courtesy of the author and of Jonathan Cape, Ltd., publishers

Princess Mary at the age of 28: Unknown artist. By courtesy of The National Portrait Gallery, London

Princess Elizabeth: Unknown artist. Windsor Castle. Copyright Reserved

Guilford Dudley, husband of Lady Jane Grey: Unknown artist. From a photograph in the Boston Athenaeum

following p. 112

Philip II of Spain, husband of Queen Mary: Titian. National Gallery, Naples. Alinari-Art Reference Bureau

Lady Frances Grey, Duchess of Suffolk, and her second husband, Adrian Stokes: Hans Eworth. Courtesy of Colonel John C. Wynne Finch

N O T E : According to The National Portrait Gallery, there is no authentic portrait of Catherine Parr or of Henry Grey, Jane's father. Portraits so named earlier have proven to be of someone else.

NOTE:

In doing research on Lady Jane Grey I found it difficult to believe that one so young could speak in a manner so adult.

No doubt this will also occur to the reader, but I have no course but to present her as she was seen by her contemporaries.

Many of her speeches given here are actual quotes.

G. M.

Three Royal Ladies

"Jane, you be queen," said Edward Tudor laughingly, "and we shall be your subjects, loyal and obedient." He picked up a twig from the lawn. "Here's your scepter."

"No!" spoke up Elizabeth in her spirited, assertive way. "*I* shall be queen! I shall be queen or I won't play."

"Oh," replied Jane sweetly, "it is a silly game. Being a queen isn't any fun. Let's play something else."

"Yes," said Mary, solemn as always, "play Hoodman Blind. Jane is right. Being a queen is not a happy state."

She sat slightly apart from the three children, yet, though much older, she was invariably a part of this intimate family foursome, especially when Jane and Edward came to Hunsdon for a visit. Some distance away in the shade, looking on indulgently, sat some of their ladies—Mary's friend and confidante, Mary Browne; Elizabeth's governess, Mrs. Ashley; Lady Margaret Bryan, Edward's governess; Jane's governess, Mrs. Ashley, sister-in-law of the first; and Mrs. Ellen, who had suckled Jane and was rarely far from her charge.

It was a pleasant, tranquil scene on that bright June day in 1543. Looming in the background was Hunsdon, with its four towers: a stately brick castle in Hertfordshire. Surrounding it was the spacious park: a place of majestic trees, a broad lawn, white pigeons soaring against the rich blue of the spring sky, and the soft sound of rooks.

Mary, Elizabeth, Edward, and Jane were not merely playing at being royal, they *were* royal; and since they knew what it meant to be royal, they readily abandoned the game Edward had suggested. Now, sobered by Mary's words, they were suddenly silent. Jane and Edward sank close beside each other on the ground, hands clasped. Elizabeth, spreading her full long skirts self-consciously, took a chair near Mary.

The world of the three younger children was entirely composed of adults. They had not been shielded from knowledge of what was taking place within it—the burnings, the hangings, the beheadings, the incessant intrigues, the jealousies, the uncertainties. Young as they were, they had already learned that there were many things not to be discussed, even with one another. They already possessed a curious, unchildlike wisdom.

It was always a happy event when, about four times a year for periods of a week or two, Jane and Edward were permitted to visit Mary and Bess at Hunsdon. When the three youngest were alone with only Mary, they played noisily, often roughly, formality abandoned. But let an adult other than their governesses approach within hearing distance, and their deportment underwent an abrupt change. They became quiet, guardedly decorous, addressing one another with the gravity, dignity, and ceremonious phrases of grownups.

They had been rigidly instructed in court etiquette. They knew which person took precedence over another; how to address anyone in accordance with the individual's rank; when to curtsy, when to kneel, and when merely to bow. In these courtesies they had been carefully schooled, but there were things they knew without being taught—for instance, that most of the adults surrounding them, with the exception of their governesses, could not be trusted.

They knew that one day a man or woman might be in high favor, rich, gay, sought after. The next day he might be missing from court and everyone would be saying dreadful things about him, for he had been sent to the Tower and would soon be beheaded. Such was the curious, unreliable, hypocritical world in which these young people were growing up. They could trust one another. Venturing beyond this might be tragic. Though Mary was much older, she was still one of them. She might reprimand them, but she would not tattle.

The one thing they had in common was a hunger for the kind of love enjoyed by nonroyal children—the love of a mother and a father. With the exception of Mary, none of them had experienced this, and she had known it only when she was very young and only for a short while.

Hunsdon Castle—a huge brick building surrounded by high, strong walls—was being allowed to deteriorate. Day by day it grew shabbier, more neglected, and there were times when even food was scarce. Serene, isolated, dingy, it was utterly removed from the feverish activities of King Henry's court.

Few visitors came there, and the young people now seated thoughtfully in the shade were expecting no one. There was Edward Tudor, only six, with small mouth and pointed chin, slender fingers and dark, sad eyes. One shoulder was slightly higher than the other. He was heir to the throne of England, yet his clothes were woefully shabby and the requests of his governess for new ones were usually ignored.

Then there was Mary, twenty-seven, and looking easily thirty—a thin, faded woman, short, pale, with primly coifed russet hair, a tight mouth, strong jaw, and a short neck. Once she had been important to her father and to his realm. Once she had been addressed as "princess." But when her father had divorced her beloved mother he had decreed that she should henceforth be addressed merely as "Lady Mary." Since then he had shown no interest in her whatsoever, and because his courtiers strove to imitate him, Mary was considered unimportant. She had grown accustomed now to being neglected. Mary, whose mother had been the lovely Catherine of Aragon and who was the granddaughter of

Ferdinand and Isabella of Spain, made no attempt to make herself attractive. She was hopelessly plain and she knew it.

In sharp contrast was her half sister, Elizabeth. She, too, had been disinherited and must now be referred to, not as princess, but as Lady Elizabeth. Though shabby, she was the exact opposite of Mary, except that she, too, was short and slender. But her eyes were animated, her lips vividly red, and her reddish hair was frizzed. Even at ten she showed a flair for dressing stylishly, wearing becoming shades and many jewels, especially pearls. Like Mary, she had an erect carriage. She was always lively, talkative, liked to play rough games, loved being gaped at.

Elizabeth's mother had not been royal. She was merely a "gentlewoman"—Anne Boleyn, King Henry's second wife, whom he had had beheaded. Her father often seemed to hate her.

Finally, there was little Jane—Lady Jane Grey, their cousin, the same age as Edward. Jane, the only one who was richly dressed, was exquisite. Looking at her now, one was aware of a fair and flawless complexion, a broad forehead, small, red mouth, arched brows, and large, dark eyes with slightly drooping lids, darkly lashed.

Jane was of the blood royal, being the grandniece of the King. Her mother's mother had been the beautiful Mary of France, Henry's younger sister, who had died in 1533, four years before Jane was born.

Jane had been named for Jane Seymour, Henry's third wife, Edward's mother, who had died soon after Edward's birth. Jane had been born a few days before Edward, in 1537.

To her, these visits to Hunsdon were holidays. Usually all the children must study, study, study. Already Jane and Bess had some knowledge of Greek as well as French and Italian.

"Come then," said the little Prince out of a prolonged, gloomy silence, "another game of hide-and-seek; or"—he looked at Jane, for he always wanted to please her—"would you rather play Hoodman Blind?" This was a game in which a hood was placed over the head of one person and the others must scamper out of his way. The one who was caught had to pay a forfeit—a kerchief, a ring, sometimes a kiss, and sometimes one would have to submit to being tickled, whereupon the others would laugh uproariously as they looked on.

"Perhaps, after all, it is better that you rest a while," advised Mary in her deep, mannish voice. "Let Jane tell us the news of London. Bess and I hear nothing. Nobody comes here. Sometimes it seems as though the King wants to forget that we exist."

No sooner had she ceased speaking than there was the sound of a trumpet and the big gates opened.

"Listen!" said Bess. "You just said that nobody comes here. It seems to me that we have a visitor."

Edward ran to the driveway and then hurried back to the group, taking his place beside Jane. "It is a messenger from the King."

"Can it be?" asked Mary. "Are you sure?"

"He wears the royal livery."

"It must be something important," said Bess.

Silently the royal youngsters formed a line, waiting for the scarlet-liveried messenger to be led toward them by one of the guards. Mary's eyes became charged with anxiety. She was no stranger to this emotion. Ever since the days when she had been torn from her mother, she had grown used to fear. She still bravely adhered to her religion, and this in itself constituted a constant danger, what with the monasteries being destroyed and priests being burned at the stake and Catholics being tortured. So many people who had dared befriend her mother had met death on the scaffold. Her turn might be next.

Jane, Edward, and Bess, brought up as Protestants, did not share Mary's peril. They waited sedately as the messenger walked jauntily toward them and bowed. The older women had risen from their places and edged forward, intent upon hearing the news that the splendidly attired courier had brought.

"You come from the King?" asked Mary in a grave, quiet tone that belied her inner fear.

In reply he handed her a letter, bowed again, and stood waiting. She read the note, holding it close to her pathetically shortsighted eyes. Then she folded it, speaking calmly.

"As the King's Grace desires, we shall be ready to leave tomorrow morning," she told him.

He bowed again and walked away, followed by the guard. When he had gone, the three children crowded about her.

"What is it, Mary?" asked Bess eagerly. "Is the news good?"

"We must make ready to go to court," she answered crisply. "At once."

"Why?" asked Edward.

"To be present at His Majesty's wedding to"—she read the name carefully—"Catherine Parr, Lady Latimer."

"He's getting married *again?*" asked Bess. "This Catherine Parr will be his sixth wife."

"Who is Lady Latimer?" asked Edward, his eyes upon Jane. "Have you heard your mother discuss her?"

"Yes," Jane answered. "Of late there has been quite a little talk about her. I heard my mother say that Lady Latimer had heard of the sorry state you and Bess and Mary lived in and had actually been bold enough to go to the King and protest!"

"That was wondrous kind," said Bess. "What else have you heard the marchioness say?"

"That Lady Latimer has recently taken a fine house in London, that she's twice widowed, and comes from Yorkshire. There was some talk, Edward, that she and your uncle, Lord Thomas Seymour, were in love. At least he called upon her often. It's odd that she has found favor with the King, because it is said that at her house the new religion, Lutheranism, is openly discussed."

"The King is against it, but both my uncles favor it," said Edward. "Well? Go on. Have you ever seen her, Jane?"

"No, but my mother doesn't think she is especially pretty, though she is said to be extremely learned. My mother will be surprised to learn that she is to be queen. In fact, when it was known that several times she visited the King at his invitation, my mother laughed and said, 'Since when has the King's Grace ever been attracted to a woman with *brains?*' "

"So Lady Latimer is to be our next queen!" said the boy.

"Poor thing!" said Bess.

"I recall once meeting her briefly," said Mary. "I liked her. Little did I think then that she would ever be my stepmother."

"I would never want to be queen," said Jane earnestly. "Never! Never!"

"Have no fear," replied Mary shortly, "you never will be."

Jane smiled. "I'm grateful for that. To be a queen—that is dangerous."

Bess nodded. She knew how dangerous it was. Hadn't her mother perished on the block? Bess never spoke of her mother, but she knew the whole sad story.

"Yes," continued Jane thoughtfully, "I'm glad that I need never fear being made a queen."

Actually, though she never thought about it, she did have some claim to the throne—through her grandmother, who had been born Mary Tudor and for whom Lady Mary had been named. Jane was well acquainted with the romantic story of Mary Tudor, the younger sister of Henry VIII. She had been a girl in her teens when Henry sent her to France to marry the aged French king, Louis XII. Elizabeth's mother, Anne Boleyn, and Edward's mother, Jane Seymour, had been Princess Mary's maids of honor.

Well, they had gone off to France where fresh, young, lovely Mary had married the feeble old monarch, only to find herself a widow a few months after the marriage. Then she had done a surprising and daring thing. Without King Henry's knowledge she had married the man she loved—dashing Charles Brandon, Duke of Suffolk, who had been sent as part of the escort to conduct the royal widow back to England. Charles Brandon had been a great favorite of King Henry and had been named Edward's godfather. But when Mary married him, the King had gone into one of his tantrums and vowed never to forgive her. It was Queen Catherine, Henry's first wife, who had finally managed to reconcile Henry with his sister and her bridegroom. Charles Brandon was still alive and had speedily married again after Mary Tudor's death.

And so Jane, granddaughter of that princess, had a connection with the throne—that is, if Edward, Mary, and Bess should die, she might be considered an heir to the crown. Of course, there was another claimant, also named Mary, the baby Queen of Scotland, granddaughter of Henry's other sister, Margaret. It was rumored that even now Henry was trying to promote a marriage between Edward and the infant Queen of Scots.

"I wish I didn't have to go home so soon," Jane said wistfully.

To get away from home was always a pleasure. Her father, Henry Grey, Marquess of Dorset, and Lady Frances, her mother, were extravagant, worldly, self-centered. They treated their eldest daughter with unnatural and unrelenting severity, even with cruelty.

Dorset House was a palace almost as imposing as those belonging to the King. Here were wealth, fashion, and lavish entertainments, but to Jane there was something lacking, something of vital necessity to her happiness. The child was hungry for love. She had two sisters. Catherine was four and a replica of her mother. Poor little Mary, an infant, was deformed and whenever possible was hidden from sight.

Their parents were utter strangers to that warm, beautiful emotion called parental love. They were usually at court, slavish in their attendance upon the King, jealous of their position. They despised what he despised and liked what he liked. Lady Frances was somewhat fleshy, with coarse, heavy features. Above all things she was proud of her Tudor ancestry, which gave her court precedence over her husband's relatives.

The Greys catered to anyone who enjoyed royal favor and mercilessly snubbed those who had fallen from it. The care of their three daughters was turned over entirely to governesses and maids.

"I wish I didn't have to go home," Jane repeated. "I like coming here."

Mary, usually undemonstrative, put her hand on the child's shoulder. "We always look forward to visits by you and Edward."

Edward lived at Havering-Bower in the care of Lady Margaret Bryan, but he was often permitted to visit his half-sisters. Though not as good a student as Jane, he, too, had started the study of languages.

The three royal children were wondering about this stranger, Catherine Parr, Lady Latimer, who would soon become Henry's sixth wife. Would this marriage make a difference in their lives? Remembering that she had already shown an interest in them, they realized that it was doubtless because of her influence that they were being invited to the wedding.

In that moment Mary remembered her mother, that saintly, queenly woman whose heart had been broken when King Henry had fallen madly in love with "the Boleyn girl." Catherine of Aragon had loved him. She had fought valiantly against the divorce, clinging desperately to Mary, her only child. Ruthlessly, the King had separated mother and daughter and had even forbidden their reunion when poor Catherine lay dying.

Mary had never ceased to revere her mother and had known only disdain for Anne Boleyn, a vivacious, witty, and impertinent creature who had shamelessly supplanted her mother in the King's affections. Next to attract him was Edward's mother—sly, tactful Jane Seymour. After her death had come Anne of Cleves, who had been Henry's wife for six months and whom he had divorced. The King's children had liked her, but they saw little of her now, since she had retired to the palace at Richmond.

Succeeding her as queen had come young Catherine Howard, who had been his bride for eighteen months and had then been beheaded. And now this stranger, Catherine Parr. Yes, as Jane had said, it was dangerous to be a queen.

Mary's reverie was interrupted by one of her ladies, Mary Browne, who curtsied before her.

"My Lady, we could scarce help overhearing. If we are to leave in the morning, should we not start packing?"

"Yes. Tell me, what do you know about Catherine Parr?"

"Very little, My Lady. She is said to be extremely attractive and immensely cultured. She was first wedded to Lord Borough, a wealthy, elderly gentleman who died shortly afterward. Next she was wedded to Lord Latimer, aged also, who died barely six months ago. They lived in Yorkshire. She is now about thirty years old."

"Three years older than I."

"And the King is fifty-two," said Jane. "So now she marries another old man!"

"Of course, we shall like her," said Bess in her sprightly, decisive way. "At least, we must pretend to. Well, come, Mary, we must get ready to leave. Would that we had better clothing in which to appear before our new stepmother!

Everything I have is woeful shoddy. I've not a decent kirtle to my name."

They strolled off, followed by their ladies, leaving Edward and Jane alone.

"Shall we play some game?" asked Jane.

Edward did not return her smile. "No, I don't feel like playing any more. I'm sorry we have to go. It is always such fun being with you. I miss you when we don't see each other. You probably don't miss me because you have your sisters."

"Oh, they're only babies. Besides, I don't play much with Catherine. She's selfish and always wants her own way and sometimes she hits me. My mother always takes her part."

"Why don't you hit her back?"

"I don't like hitting people. Besides, she tells my father and then he hits me, too."

"Poor Jane. I wish I were older. I'd fight anyone who hurt you. All those black-and-blue marks on your arms! When I'm king I shall punish anyone who hurts you. I'll send them to the Tower and have them killed. I love you more than anyone in all the world, Jane, even more than Mary and Bess."

"I love you, too, Edward," she confessed with the sweet simplicity of childhood. "I wish we could be together every minute. I love you more than . . . more than . . ." Words failed her.

"Do you like many grown-up people? I don't. I don't like your father and mother, the way they smile at me. I don't like my uncle, Edward Seymour, either. He's mean and cruel and stingy."

"Don't you even like Thomas Seymour, your other uncle?"

"Yes, I like him. He's jolly. Generous, too. Sometimes he gives me money. Jane, what did you say about his being in love with Catherine Parr?"

"I heard my parents talking about your uncle and Lady

Latimer one day. They said they expected them to announce their plight-troth, but that couldn't have been true, because now she's going to marry the King."

"Perhaps it was only what grownups call gossip. Anyhow, I think we had better not mention it."

At the thought of being separated, these children, lonely and unloved, felt like bursting into tears. Edward fought against his emotion, knowing that tears were unmanly, and now he was relieved when Lady Margaret came to announce that it was time for His Highness to take a nap. Obediently he followed her, not looking back at Jane.

Dinner that night followed the usual procedure. Mary sat at one table with the three children, while their governesses and ladies sat slightly apart at another. Talk was focused entirely upon the King's approaching marriage. Everyone was eager to see the woman who was to be their queen, and all of them thought of Henry's other weddings, though they were careful not to mention them.

Mary had been present when her father had married Jane Seymour. She had known Jane even before the marriage and had rather liked her. Edward, she thought, resembled his mother. She had been present, too, among that great company of nobles at Edward's baptism when Queen Jane, already dying, had been carried into the chapel at Hampton Court. What a magnificent scene that was! Bess had been there, too: a vivacious four-year-old. Jane's grandfather, the Duke of Suffolk, had carried the canopy over the infant prince. Later, as chief mourner, Mary had held watch over Queen Jane's body.

Yes, Mary had many memories, all of them unhappy. How badly Henry had treated Anne of Cleves, only twenty-four when she came to England, calling her his "great Flanders mare." A tall, friendly woman was Anne, with a pockmarked face. And Jane's mother had made cruel fun of her. How could a woman like Frances Grey have a child so sweet, so gentle and endearing, as Jane?

"The Lady Mary is very silent," said Bess, reverting to formality because of the presence of adults.

"I was thinking of the past," Mary answered.

"Why think of that?" asked Bess. "Tomorrow we're off to court. I would that we had some decent clothes to wear."

"You think too much about clothes. Life is a serious thing. Tonight when we go to our rooms we must all pray for the happiness of the new queen."

"I wonder what sort of person she is," said Bess. "I wonder what she looks like."

"Forever thinking about looks!"

Bess was vain, like her father and mother, vain and clever, opinionated and often sly. Edward, on the other hand, was the direct opposite of his father. Mary had often felt a somewhat maternal emotion toward Bess, but lately she had begun to mistrust her. Jane was of different caliber. Mary, starved for love, feeling herself an alien because of her steadfast faith in her Catholic religion, had for Jane an affection she was careful not to betray.

Jane was looking at Edward, her dark eyes almost worshipful. She was not thinking of the past but of the future, of the time when Edward would be king. To her, Edward was wonderful, a being who could do no wrong.

When he is king, she thought pensively, everything will be good. When he is king there'll be no beheadings or burnings. I hope they don't make him marry the Queen of Scotland. When I grow up I shall marry Edward. No, because then I would have to be queen.

Her big, long-lashed eyes went to Elizabeth. She remembered that her father's mother, Margaret, Dowager Lady Dorset, had been one of Anne Boleyn's closest friends and had carried Bess to the baptismal font. Lady Dorset had died two years ago, but Jane remembered her saying how fascinating and hot-tempered Bess's mother had been. Bess, now—ah, Bess would actually *enjoy* being queen!

Next her gaze traveled to Mary—puny, sickly, somber Mary—who, though there was no gaiety in her, loved to gamble. It was difficult to imagine Mary on the throne. And if, by some strange quirk of fate, such a thing ever happened England, Jane thought, would not be a happy place.

"Of what is Your Ladyship thinking?" asked Bess. "Whatever it is, it must be very sad. Come, cheer up. Tomorrow Lady Mary and I will forget our monotony for a while. We're off to a wedding!"

"You always love to be going somewhere," said Mary.

"True," laughed Bess, her eyes sparkling as she raised a mug of milk, holding it high. "To the new Queen—and may she keep her head!"

Catherine

Escorted by sixty men-at-arms, two maids, nurse, and governess, Jane arrived home to find that her parents were at court. In spite of the fact that there were over a hundred servants, the huge mansion seemed empty except for the two liveried butlers who opened the heavy doors. Dorset House was a mansion in Westminster, not far from Whitehall. Its broad terrace overlooked the Thames.

Jane's apartment, on the second floor in the north wing, consisted of a huge sitting room with tapestried walls and stained-glass windows, in addition to a group of small rooms for her personal attendants. The furniture was of dark, heavy oak, deeply carved. A large stone fireplace dominated this room; in no way did it indicate that it belonged to a child except that a wooden doll, imported from France, sat in one corner of an upholstered window seat.

Opening off from the sitting room was her bedchamber, with another fireplace, an enormous poster bed, chairs, a table, and several richly carved oak chests. When she had washed and changed her clothes, a butler brought a tray with food, which he placed on the table.

"Will there be anything else, My Lady?" he asked stiffly.

"No, Potter. Thank you."

As he was leaving, little Catherine entered. At four, she was as tall as Jane and spoke as precisely as though she were ten years older.

"Did Your Ladyship have a good time?"

"Pleasant. As always."

"Why wouldn't they let me go, too?"

"Because Your Ladyship is too young." Jane seated herself at the table.

"Too young! I suppose neither of us will be allowed to go to the King's wedding. We'll both be too young for that, too, although Mother said Edward, Mary, and Bess were invited. Why should they be invited and we not asked?"

"Because they are the King's children. We are only his grandnieces."

"I wish I would grow up. I want to go to court, too."

There was the sound of horses' hoofs in the stone courtyard and the sisters ran to the window overlooking it. They gazed down upon a richly dressed group of people whom the Dorset grooms were assisting from the backs of splendidly caparisoned horses. In addition to their parents, there were their father's two young brothers, Lord Thomas and Lord John Grey, and their wives; Viscount Lisle and his lady; Jane's grandfather, Charles Brandon, Duke of Suffolk, and Catherine, his young wife; Edward Seymour, the Earl of Hertford, and his wife Anne; Thomas Cranmer, Archbishop of Canterbury, and several other important personages.

Jane sighed. She was hungry and tired from her journey, but she knew that as soon as her parents were settled in the great hall, they would summon her and subject her to the usual cross-examination.

She was not puzzled as to why they should want to know what had been said at Hunsdon, for be it good or bad, they would have something to tell King Henry. Though he had not the slightest love for his daughters, he was always interested in discovering any insubordination or any remarks, flattering or otherwise, that they might make about him.

Jane had not long to wait before a manservant announced in his cold and correct way that Her Ladyship was wanted in the great hall. Lifting her long, full skirts in one hand so as to walk more freely, Jane descended the wide stone stairway and faced the company with no display of shyness or embarrassment.

Immediately following Jane's deep curtsy, Lady Frances spoke, her voice sharp and cold. She was a handsome woman, and her jewels and clothing, always magnificent, were chosen to make her appear younger than her age. Her face was slightly puffy, and no amount of cosmetics could hide the coarseness of her skin.

On the other side of the room sat Henry Grey, a thin man in his early thirties. He was of medium height with a small, neatly clipped chin beard, an impressive brown mustache, waxed until it stood out thin and rigid on either side of his lean face, and sparse, light brown hair.

If either of these people realized that their eldest daughter was making a good impression on their guests, they gave no sign of it. Jane always had the uncomfortable feeling that nothing she might say or do would be approved by her parents.

"Your Ladyship will repeat what was said by Lady Mary and Lady Elizabeth," her mother said at once.

"Madam, we talked of nothing but our games and our lessons."

"Stupid!" exclaimed her father. "Of course they discussed His Majesty. What opinion did they voice with regard to the marriage?"

The company waited expectantly. All these people were showily dressed, each trying to exceed the other in elegance. Jane's parents had this in common with each other—the love of dress, the ambition to shine socially, to associate with the right people, such as the Seymours, Thomas Cranmer, and especially the King. The King's moods, beliefs, and friends were theirs, and in this they conformed with the rest of their peculiar world. Their fortunes, their well-being, their position, their happiness depended solely upon the King. They were careful to voice no opinion other than his.

Resent this puppet-like existence? It never occurred to them. No matter what might be their inner, personal convictions, to show pity or even the slightest partisanship for anyone who displeased Henry would have been suicidal, even though that person might be their close friend or relative. This was their code.

Being courtiers was their full-time occupation, leaving no interludes to give to their daughters. They were glad that Jane was beautiful and a brilliant student, but the child was so different from themselves that she invariably exasperated them. They supplied her with excellent tutors. They saw to it that she had gorgeous clothing and jewels. This they considered their sole duty toward her.

Catherine was her mother's favorite. Though pretty, she was not as lovely as Jane. Temperamentally and physically she resembled her mother, and consequently, though she was rarely caressed, she was never abused.

Jane knew that she was expected to serve as a spy when she visited the King's daughters, but since she considered Mary and Bess her friends, she invariably disappointed her parents by answering their queries evasively.

"Well?" cried Henry Grey, incensed by his daughter's silence. "Speak up! Have you a tongue in your head? They must have voiced an opinion."

"Sir, we talked mostly about lessons. We wished the Lady Latimer well."

Infuriated, Lady Frances grabbed her daughter by the shoulder and shook her roughly. "Did I not warn you when you left for Hunsdon to keep your ears and eyes open? What did the Lady Mary say when she learned the King was to marry again?"

"Madam, I . . . I don't recall."

"She must have said something," said Edward Seymour, a lean, sour-faced man in his late thirties. "Did she cross herself? Did she take out her rosary? She called him a sinner,

perchance? The King has no liking either for her or for Elizabeth. Did she comment upon this? Do either of them rebel?
I think the Lady Jane is not quite so dim-witted as she seems."

"My Lord, I don't remember ever seeing her cross herself.
She and Lady Elizabeth said only that they wished the King's
Grace joy. They drank to the health of the new Queen. They
were pleased that they had been invited to the wedding."

"Her tutors say this child is a precocious scholar," said Lady
Frances angrily, "but sometimes one would doubt that she
has any brains at all. Catherine is quite different. When
Catherine is old enough to visit Hunsdon we shall have a full
report." She turned to Jane. "You may go to your room," she
said icily.

Breathing a sigh of relief, Jane curtsied and left the room.
It would probably be a long time before she saw her parents
again, and that was something to be grateful for.

During the next few weeks she frequently marveled that
her attendants, Mrs. Ellen and Mrs. Ashley, knew so much
about what went on at court. One morning while her maid
was brushing her long, light brown hair and a chamber-
woman was putting her laundry in a basket, she learned that
the Queen had given Mary a magnificent pair of gold brace-
lets set with rubies. A few days later she heard that the new
Queen was much liked and that through her influence with
the King, his daughters had been restored to their proper
rank and that it was now correct to address them as princesses.

"She must be very good, very kind," said Jane as her maid
brought her jewel casket and held it open for her to choose
the gems she would wear that day.

"Yes, Your Ladyship. All reports agree as to that. 'Tis said
that she is without flaws, that the King dotes on her, that her
royal stepchildren are already fond of her. Everyone hopes
that at last the King's Grace had found a wife who will not
meet the fate of the others. We—"

She was interrupted by the entrance of another maid. "Oh," said the newcomer, "Her Ladyship is already dressed." She spoke to Jane's maid. "You'll have to undress Her Ladyship and see that she wears something suitable for court. The Lady Frances orders you to be quick about it."

"I'm to go to court?" asked Jane, her dark eyes bright with excitement.

"Queen Catherine has requested that Your Ladyship pay her a visit."

There was a flurry now to get Jane dressed, and Mrs. Ashley was called in for advice. The red velvet gown? The blue brocade? The yellow? The white? When at last Jane was ready, she went down the stairs to find her mother waiting in the great hall. Lady Frances looked her daughter over and for once could find no fault.

Children dressed precisely as did their elders, and Jane wore a brocaded floor-length gown of blue with a silver girdle and a close-fitting French hood, also blue, with a blue veil hanging to her waist in the back. Her jewelry consisted of sapphires and diamonds. Lady Frances also wore brocade, though hers was yellow, with a high, silver brocade stand-away collar that flared at the nape of her neck. Her fashionable close-fitting hood was richly embroidered about the face with pearls. Her necklaces were of pearls, ropes and ropes of them. Her gloves were orange leather.

Leaving the house, they stepped into an ornate palanquin that was carried on the shoulders of eight men in lavender velvet doublets. Surrounding them as they left the courtyard was a guard of almost a hundred men, also in lavender. The litter was gilt, with blue satin cushions.

It was a warm day in late July and the clothing the two ladies wore made it seem even warmer. Passers-by stared admiringly at the litter and its occupants, drawing aside respectfully and wondering who these personages were. Lady Frances held her head high and haughtily ignored the stares. For a time neither she nor her daughter spoke.

"Mind your manners," she commanded at last coldly. "You know what to do. A low curtsy to the Queen. Should His Majesty chance to enter, kneel before him. I need not tell you that it is important to make a favorable impression. Do not be timid. The King is always impatient with timidity. Flatter him. He thrives upon it."

"I shall try to do well, Madame. Tell me, does Your Ladyship like the Queen? I mean really like her?"

"She is charming." Lady Frances said this about every queen—until she fell from grace. "The King is quite mad about her. But then, he was mad about all his wives, except that German *Hausfrau*, Anne of Cleves. I must say Queen Catherine is different from the others. She has been wondrous kind to the Princesses Mary and Elizabeth, giving them many presents, seeing to it that they have suitable clothing and increased allowances. Since they have returned to the country, she had sent them many gifts and shows an interest in their studies. It is to be hoped that she will take a fancy to you. I cannot impress upon Your Ladyship too strongly that it is of the utmost importance that she do so."

"Yes, Madame, but how does one make oneself liked?"

"By saying the things that please Their Majesties, by agreeing with them. This is the only way to get on in the world. Never forget that."

"No, Madame."

Nothing more was said until they reached Westminster Palace. Jane was thrilled as they were helped from the palanquin before that fabulous building. She had often seen it from the outside but this was the first time she had entered it. Nowadays it was not used much, for King Henry preferred Whitehall.

Men-at-arms stood rigidly at intervals. Two menservants in

Tudor livery had opened the huge doors as the marchioness and her daughter approached them. A third bowed before the visitors.

"The Marchioness will please wait in the anteroom. Her Ladyship is to follow me."

"What?" cried Lady Frances in a tone of displeasure and surprise. "Am I not to be included?"

"Her Majesty wishes to see Her Ladyship alone."

"Very well." Waiting in the anteroom was not without its compensations, for there would be many courtiers, male and female, and consequently there would be gossip. The servant led her to it, though she knew the way.

Jane followed another man up the long flight of stairs lighted by a series of resin torches, their yellow, flickering glow adding a touch of solemnity to the occasion.

She was shown into a large room hung with beautiful tapestries. It was empty except for the small figure of Edward, who, because of the presence of the servant, bowed gravely.

"Your Highness," Jane said softly as she sank gracefully to her knees.

When the guide had left, she rose and the two children rushed toward each other, arms outstretched.

"Edward! Oh, I'm so glad you're here! Tell me, do you like her?"

The boy's blue eyes suddenly filled with tears. "She is my good mother," he said in a voice close to veneration. His emotion was explained by the fact that this was the first time he had known a mother's tenderness. Already he had learned to mistrust most of the adults who surrounded him, and Catherine's coming had filled a deep void in his young, love-starved life.

"I'm so glad you're fond of her!"

"You'll love her, too. I told her all about you. I think that's why she sent for you."

"What did you tell her about me?"

He grinned. "I won't tell you."

Laughingly she began pummeling him with her fists. "You will! You will!"

Also laughing, he ducked her blows and the two began a hilarious chase about the room, he crying out, "I won't! I won't!" and she, holding her long skirts high so as not to impede her, replying, "You will! You will!"

Their game ended abruptly as the big double doors to the corridor opened and a lady entered the room: not a very tall lady—she was actually five feet three; not very thin, but certainly not stout; a trim, matronly figure displaying excellent, though conservative, taste in dress. Catherine Parr had small, well-modeled features, a high, serene brow, golden hair naturally curly, and a fair complexion. Her eyes were hazel—bright, kind, honest eyes. Her eyebrows were well marked and her mouth was soft, smiling, lovely. To Jane she seemed the most beautiful woman in the world.

Instead of bowing, Edward ran toward her, putting his hand in hers, while Jane knelt.

"My sweet mother," said the boy proudly, "this is my cousin, the Lady Jane Grey."

"And your best friend, eh? Rise, Jane, and come here."

As Jane smilingly approached her, Catherine looked down at her in gentle scrutiny. The child's only resemblance to the Tudors was her fair complexion and the glint of gold in her hair. Her eyes were deep, soulful, candid. Her features were delicate and flawlessly balanced. Her smile, brilliant and engaging, revealed small but perfect teeth. Her tiny hands were slender and sensitive. Her fingers flashed with several costly rings.

"So this is Jane," said the Queen with a fond, slow smile as she opened her arms.

With those soft arms about her, Jane felt that she, too, had found "a sweet mother."

There was no formality. Catherine seated herself on a

couch with Edward at her left and Jane at her right, both clinging to her hands. She wanted to know what Jane was studying and was amazed at how precocious the child was.

Despite her knowledge, Jane was anything but a prig, nor was she boastful and a show-off. What the Queen immediately perceived was the child's sweetness and simplicity. As their eyes met, both knew they would love each other. And Edward beamed as he realized this.

Before attracting the attention of the King, Catherine had been the wife of two elderly men, both of whom had had children. She had mothered these children; she had devotedly nursed their fathers during their last illnesses. Now her affection centered upon Jane, delightful and appealing, the sort of daughter she had always longed for.

She was a friendly person as well as a wise one. She had not become haughty or arrogant when she became queen. In fact, she had been reluctant to assume this exalted position. Though she treated the Greys amicably, she knew their ilk, knew them to be ambitious, inwardly merciless, intent only upon pleasing important persons. They would appear to approve of her heartily only as long as she held the affection of the King. This sweet, modest child seemed not to belong to them at all, and she sensed Jane's need for affection.

Edward had, indeed, told her about Jane, talking of her with enthusiasm, and now she understood why. She wanted to keep this small, winsome creature from becoming like her parents.

From time to time as they talked she put her arm about the child's shoulders, smiling into Jane's frankly adoring eyes. For over an hour they spoke, mostly about the two children's studies. Catherine impressed upon them the importance of learning and gently chided Edward for his poor penmanship.

"I shall practice to do better," he promised, eager for her

approval. "When I go back to Havering I will write you often and you shall see how I improve."

"I shall be happy to receive your letters." She looked up as a page opened the door.

"His Majesty, the King," he announced.

Instantly the mood changed. The three on the couch rose and sank to their knees. Then the doorway was filled with a man so tall, so broad, that to Jane he seemed a giant; a man with a fat, oily face, small, glittering eyes, and a small mouth that seemed even smaller because of a red mustache and beard. His strong legs were clad in white and he wore the Order of the Garter below his left knee. Henry the Eighth was an impressive presence.

Behind him was a retinue of men and women whom Jane had often seen at her parents' home. There was Sir Thomas Wriothesley, the King's chief counsellor; Stephen Gardiner, Bishop of Winchester; Thomas Cranmer; Edward Seymour and his wife Anne; Thomas Seymour; Jane's parents; and Lady Anne Herbert, who was Queen Catherine's sister and one of her maids of honor.

The King, his fat fingers blazing with enormous rings, smiled affectionately at his wife, his son, and his grandniece. He strode toward them and helped Catherine to her feet.

"How now, sweetheart," he said in a loud, laughing voice as he kissed her.

Then, holding her hand, he walked to the couch with her. When they were seated he motioned to the others to find seats, but most of them had to remain standing, for there were insufficient stools and it was improper for anyone to sit in a chair when the King was present.

"Rise, Lady Jane," he said, staring at her with his bright, beady eyes. "You are very like your grandmother." His face sobered at the memory of the sister he had loved. "Yes, very like her." He gazed up at Jane's father. "Henry, you have a little beauty here."

"I am honored if my daughter pleases Your Majesty. I am glad to say that her tutors declare her to be an excellent student."

Henry the King, Henry the all-powerful, turned his attention back to Jane. He had no love for his daughters, perhaps because they reminded him of their mothers; but with Jane he had no such memories.

"Yes, she is the image of Mary. So, you like to study, eh, little one? Tell me, can you read the New Testament in Greek?"

"Yes, my liege."

"That is remarkable. She must come to see us often, eh, Kate?"

"I was hoping Your Majesty would desire it," replied the Queen meekly.

After this, though Jane remained at court for four hours, she and Edward found themselves ignored by their elders. They drew aside, standing together near one of the windows.

"I love her," Jane whispered to him happily. "I love her more than anyone in the whole world."

His small mouth puckered in a pout. "Even more than me?"

"Oh, no! But next to you."

"I shall probably not see you again for a long time. I'm to leave for Havering in the morning."

"I wish you didn't have to go away. But even if I don't see you, I sometimes pretend that you're with me. And I always pray for you. Oh, Edward, Edward, I think everything is going to be much happier for us, now that we have Queen Catherine!"

"Yes," he agreed.

The King's House

After that first meeting with the King and his bride Jane became more at ease in the royal palaces than she had ever been in her own home, for Catherine seemingly could not bear to be parted from her.

She would send for the child and keep her for weeks, an arrangement that met with Henry's hearty approval. This boisterous, ponderous man was responsible for terrible deeds, what with monasteries being destroyed by his orders, churches razed, priests burned, and courtiers who displeased him being beheaded without fair trials. He was an absolute monarch. Parliament was his tool. Preachers could not give sermons containing anything at variance with his opinions. Yet Jane Grey experienced nothing from him but kindness and affection. It was difficult for her to believe the terrible reports of his unscrupulous doings, for those bloated, powerful hands were gentle and fond when they touched her head. When he smiled at her it was a jolly smile. She and Catherine were the only people in the realm who had no fear of him.

She wished she might see more of Edward, but he had returned to his own palace and rarely visited his father. Mary and Bess, too, though Catherine corresponded with them and saw to it that they lacked nothing, rarely came to London.

Jane's associates now were her tutors, the hangers-on at court, and especially the royal couple. On pleasant days when Their Majesties would stroll in the garden with a retinue of courtiers trailing behind them, Jane walked beside them, her hand in Catherine's.

Outwardly the Queen was serene and gracious, unfailingly kind to everyone, but her position was a difficult one. She knew the malice and cruelty of the man she had married, though as far as she was concerned he remained gallant and devoted; but Henry was already a sick man and required her to be almost incessantly at his service. Night after night she sat up with him, reading to him or massaging his painful, swollen leg. He would have no other nurse. Kate alone could make the many poultices he needed.

He seemed to delight in having spirited arguments with her. None of his other wives had dared disagree with him, none had been so stimulating in conversation, none had had an intellect matching his, for Henry VIII was a very learned man.

Catherine knew that among those who fawned upon her were a few who waited hopefully for her to make some mistake and thus incur the displeasure of the fickle, irascible King. She had been shocked and alarmed when Henry first told her of his love, but to have refused to marry him might have cost her her life. So she had given up the man she really loved—gay, flirtatious Tom Seymour, the King's brother-in-law and gentleman of his privy chamber, who was called "the Adonis of the court" and who was now admiral of the Channel fleet.

Nowadays, since they saw each other daily, they had to be constantly on guard not to look at each other lest their eyes betray them. This added to the Queen's difficulties.

She must be constantly alert to pacify Henry's ferocious temper, which was apt to erupt at any moment and could assume volcanic proportions. These angers, growing more frequent day by day, were not mere explosions of wrath, likely to vanish quickly and harmlessly. They might mean the head of some erstwhile favorite. The man Catherine Parr had mar-

ried was utterly devoid of conscience. He had sent two of
his wives to the block on framed-up charges, and there were
those at court, such as Stephen Gardiner, Edward and Anne
Seymour, and Sir Thomas Wriothesley, now lord chancellor,
who waited watchfully for Catherine to meet the same fate.

To facilitate his divorce from his first wife, Catherine of
Aragon, Henry had named himself head of the Church and
decreed the practice of Catholicism to be illegal; and now,
with equal intensity, he frowned upon the growing interest
in Lutheranism. Catherine was a Lutheran. He had known
this when he married her, but he had chosen to overlook it.
But Wriothesley didn't and Gardiner didn't. They knew that
the Queen read Lutheran books, that she shared such literature with her sister, Lady Herbert, and that Edward and Jane,
through Catherine's influence, had accepted this religion.
The Queen was pious and sincere. She was a good, faithful
wife, and they would never be able to accuse her of anything
other than her devotion to this new creed.

Catherine had been queen for a year and Their Majesties
were at Hampton Court when one day Jane ran to her in
alarm. The Queen was alone with Lady Herbert.

"What is it, my dear?" Catherine asked in her gentle way.
"Come, tell me. What has frightened you?"

"Madame, my rooms have been searched!"

Catherine and her sister exchanged meaningful glances.

"Mine, too," said Lady Herbert. "Her Majesty and I were
just talking about it."

"Who did it?" asked Jane. "And why? Why?"

"I'm certain it was done on Wriothesley's orders," answered
Catherine composedly. "His minions are seeking Lutheran
books. Did they find any?"

"Not in my rooms," replied Jane. "I had hidden them behind the tapestry."

"And mine were hidden in the torch niches," said Lady
Herbert.

The three read these forbidden books, some of which were only pamphlets, and discussed them at length. The Queen's private apartments could not be searched, but there was much Lutheran literature there. Knowing this, Jane began to tremble. If anything should happen to Catherine!

"Don't let yourselves be disturbed," said the Queen soothingly. "Hereafter, though, after you have finished with the books, bring them to me. Those who seek them are not really aiming at you, but at me."

"Why should anyone want to hurt you?" asked Jane, her eyes filling with tears.

Catherine drew her close, smoothing the soft, lustrous hair. "Don't be afraid, child. We will pretend to be ignorant of the fact that your rooms have been searched. There has been no harm done."

"But why should Sir Thomas Wriothesley want to hurt you?" persisted Jane.

"You see, he is the leader of the antipapal reform party. That means those who uphold the various Catholic rites, yet deny the supremacy of the Pope. He is also against Lutheranism for the simple reason that the King is against it."

"What would have happened had he found those books in my rooms or Lady Herbert's?"

"That would have been a triumph for him, don't you see? He would have gone to the King, accusing me for having given you the books. What he has done is no surprise to me. Two weeks after my marriage I learned that he was waiting for me to make some open mistake."

"But by what right did he search our rooms?" asked Lady Herbert, keeping her voice steady only by a tremendous effort. "I know that the King has given him permission to search any house where he thinks these books are to be found, but His Majesty made an exception to any search of his own palaces. Obviously this came from his desire to protect you, Kate. Several people have been killed for possessing such books. I say Wriothesley had no right to make this search! If you reported this to the King . . ."

"Yes," said Jane, "the King loves you very much. You could have Sir Thomas put in prison!"

"I do not believe in vengeance," Catherine replied. "Haven't we read that we must pray for our enemies? Come, now, recite some Greek verses. Let me see how well you are doing."

While Jane obeyed, the Queen took up her embroidery, looking up from time to time to nod at the child, pleased with her progress.

In the midst of Jane's recital her sister Catherine was admitted. The Queen took an interest in both children, but Jane remained much closer to her, a fact that filled little Catherine with jealousy. Finally the Queen, having an appointment with the Spanish ambassador, left them, followed as usual by Lady Herbert. They watched as she walked away, superbly dressed in a kirtle of pink brocade with long, flowing sleeves lined with crimson satin and trimmed with bands of crimson velvet.

"I shall ask Mother to have a gown like that made for me," said Catherine. Then, coming close to her sister, she whispered, "She says I must tell you not to read any forbidden books, or if you do, not to let anyone know about it."

"I shall be careful," answered Jane guardedly.

"Are you reading them?"

"Yes. Come, let's read some Greek poetry." She picked up a book.

"No. I hate to study. Mother says she can't understand why Their Majesties prefer you to me."

"It's only because I'm older."

From behind them there boomed a loud, irritable voice. "Where is the Queen?"

Turning, they saw King Henry, looking taller and more obese than ever in a short, pleated gown of scarlet-and-gold brocade, with a jeweled dagger at his waist. Before they could reply or even before they rose from their kneeling position, he sat down heavily, his huge, bulging red-clad legs apart.

"What are you reading, Jane?"

She knew he suspected that it might be a Lutheran tract. Smiling, she handed the book to him. He glanced at it, motioned her away, and groaned, for the pain in his legs was especially aggravating that day.

"Greek verse. Read to me."

Seating herself on a low stool nearby, she began to read freely and easily in a low, beautifully modulated voice. Several times the King corrected her on the pronunciation of a word, then nodded for her to continue. She stopped only when Lord Thomas Seymour entered, smiling a wide, magnetic smile as he knelt before the King.

"This is an amazing child, Thomas," said Henry. "Seven years old, and she reads as well as an adult."

"She is my favorite lady," said Lord Thomas, with a bow to Jane. "Were she a little older, I would pay my court to her."

As he spoke, Catherine entered, followed by her ladies. Lord Thomas bowed low, keeping his eyes on the floor. Catherine, apparently taking no notice of him, walked to the King and kissed him on the forehead. His hand reached out for hers and he pulled her down until she sat on the arm of his chair.

"Catherine, my love, my sweet," he murmured, relaxed in her presence, all smiles now, "reprimand this rogue! I share with him and his brother the spoils of the monasteries, and what do they do? Gamble for the highest stakes, frittering away fortunes at the gaming tables."

Catherine did not look at Thomas. "Sire," she answered, "what he does is none of my affair." But she blushed ever so slightly. "What concerns me is Your Majesty's health. I think the King's Grace is feeling somewhat poorly today. Shall I call for the musicians to divert my liege?"

Thereafter things passed as usual. In the King's palaces were hundreds of pages, some liveried in white satin, others in scarlet and gold. There were fifty cooks and one hundred scullions—and always there were spies. Any thoughtless phrase was likely to be repeated to the King, and the next day one might be in prison.

King Henry had always been an excellent sportsman and a lover of music, so there was much music, dancing, tennis, bowls, quoits, hunting, hawking, archery, wrestling, even cockfighting; yet Henry was also intensely religious. Grace was said before meals, and the court was faithful in its church attendance. Lent was always firmly observed.

For Jane there were bleak intervals when she was separated from Catherine, as when she and her family paid visits to her mother's father, Charles Brandon, Duke of Suffolk; when they visited Princess Mary, now at Newhall; and when they sojourned at their Dorset country residence, Bradgate, three miles from Leicester Town, where Jane had been born.

She had always loved the old house, surrounded by twenty-five miles of park, with its many beeches, its fishpond, trout stream, woods, wide terraces, and the finest gardens in England.

The Greys never traveled with less than fifty armed men on horseback in addition to an assortment of maids, valets, secretaries, and other servants, and followed by numerous wagons containing luggage. Once this vast cavalcade went to visit Edward, who was now living at Oatlands, but the two children had no chance to be alone.

Sometimes at Bradgate or at the other castles visited by the Greys, Jane met Lady Anne Seymour and her brother, children of Edward and Anne Seymour, but usually her companions were adults, and Jane could scarcely wait to return to Catherine Parr, the one grownup who loved her and whom she loved with increasing devotion.

So 1544 came to an end, and when 1545 was ushered in by blustery winds it seemed to Jane that the years would go on and on, unchanged forever. It was now two years since she had seen Edward, but her love for the prince remained, and she still considered him, next to Catherine, her best friend in the world.

Mary and Bess came to court rarely, but the Queen carefully scrutinized Elizabeth's written lessons and frequently wrote to her, Mary, and Edward, sending them presents. Bess, now twelve, was more vivacious than ever. Mary, twenty-nine, was growing more and more serious, more and more engrossed in her religion, and determined to save Jane from what she termed "heresy."

From the beginning of the year, Jane had been back at Hampton Court with Their Majesties. Of all the King's palaces, Jane preferred this one, with its magnificent crystal chandeliers, two hundred and eighty-four guest rooms, Oriental carpets, silver basins and ewers. Henry must always have the best of everything.

The King's condition was growing worse. He could scarcely walk at all now and almost always had to be carried in a chair.

Catherine was looking tired. Henry required her presence constantly, day and night, declaring that only her soft hands could apply the poultices or massage his abscessed leg. Always tactful, always charming, always patient, she made no objection to such servitude, though it amounted to outright slavery.

The King was now so corpulent that it was impossible for him to take part in sports, and this enforced inactivity made him even more restless, more implacable. He was a difficult invalid. It seemed to Jane, now nine, that he was always in a frenzy about something. Only Catherine could soothe him. Her influence, instead of diminishing, as Wriothesley and

Gardiner had hoped, was increasing. More and more the King depended upon this woman.

As had been the case two years earlier, the conspirators could not accuse Catherine of anything. Her only "sin," if it could be so called, was her religion. That summer they arrested a beautiful gentlewoman named Anne Askew, twenty-five years old, a devout Lutheran.

To Catherine, this arrest was deeply disturbing. She had received Anne privately, talked with her at length, and though there was a legal statute against reading "heretical works," had accepted various tracts and books from her.

Anne's life had been blameless and devoted to good works. In arresting and torturing this gentle soul, Lord Chancellor Wriothesley hoped to compel her to implicate the Queen. This would enable him to accuse Catherine publicly of disobedience to the King and thus force Henry to get rid of her.

Wriothesley had private information that Lady Frances, Jane, and Lady Herbert, the Queen's sister, had been present at those meetings in the Queen's apartment, and he himself put Anne on the rack and mercilessly applied the screws to force a confession from her. Her supposed affiliation with the Queen was what made her punishment all the more diabolical, but try as he would, torture her day after day with every cruel implement at his command, Anne refused to name the Queen or any of the court ladies.

Catherine could do nothing to intervene, for not only her own life but those of Jane and others were at stake. As Wriothesley's scheme failed, his fury was unbounded. He suspected, and rightly, that from time to time the Queen managed somehow to send Anne money, yet he could not prove it. By King Henry's orders the poor girl was stretched on the rack, and by his orders she and numerous others of her faith were finally burned at the stake.

Wriothesley's failure made him all the more determined, and his chance came one day when Their Majesties were at Whitehall, a day when Henry was especially tormented by pain. Wriothesley and Gardiner had reminded him that his own household was riddled with heresy, and the King was brooding about this charge when Catherine entered.

Soon the King and Queen were embarked upon one of their spirited arguments, which had started when Gardiner congratulated Henry upon the fact that he had forbidden the people to read a new translation of the Bible. To Catherine this prohibition was all the more unreasonable because Henry himself had given the license to make the translation!

Feeling keenly that it was wrong to make it unlawful for people to read this work, Catherine began to state her views with her usual wisdom and brilliance. Henry, though a renowned theologian, found himself bested at every point. Presently Catherine realized that he had lapsed into sulky silence and that his little eyes were regarding her in a new way. Tactfully, she left the room.

Fuming, Henry turned to Wriothesley. "Women have become clerks!" he roared. "Am I in my old age to be taught by my wife?"

Here was the conspirators' opportunity. Gardiner began to make insinuations against the Queen which Henry at another time would have resented. Quick to sense his advantage, Gardiner continued.

"Your Majesty excels all the princes of this and every other age, as well as the doctors of divinity, insomuch that it is unseemly for any of your subjects to argue with you as the Queen has just done! It is grievous for your counselors to listen. Those, like the Queen, who are so bold in words would not scruple to proceed to acts of disobedience. Oh, Your Majesty, I could make great discoveries were I not deterred by the Queen's powerful faction!"

"I give you leave to make such discoveries as you can!"

"I have your permission, then, my liege," interposed Wriothesley quickly, "to draw up articles against the Queen?"

"Yes! And if you find aught against her, I shall sign her death warrant!"

When, for several days after this, Catherine was not summoned to the King's bedchamber, she became worried. Her suspicions were verified when Gardiner and Wriothesley cross-examined Lady Herbert and the other ladies who were in attendance upon the Queen.

Then, one afternoon while Jane was studying in her own room, Wriothesley, Gardiner, and several secretaries burst in upon her. She realized at once why they had come. Though she knew she must betray no fear, her heart began beating furiously.

Their eyes were cold, their faces stern, their voices brusque. They were not courtiers now; they were inquisitors, and it did not matter that they were dealing with the child whom the King regarded as a favorite. Some of the men tore into her closets as well as into the big oak chests. They searched every part of her room, while Gardiner and Wriothesley, commanding her to stand before them, began their questioning.

Jane Grey was the very soul of honesty, incapable of guile, yet now she realized that if she were to save Catherine's life she must lie—and lie convincingly.

Death of a Tyrant

"Yes, My Lords, I am a Lutheran. . . . No, I made the decision myself. The Queen has used no force or argument in converting me. . . . No, no, gentlemen, Her Majesty has never given me any such books. . . . No, sir, I never saw Anne Askew talking to the Queen. . . ."

"Look me in the face!" cried Wriothesley wrathfully. "Can you expect me to believe that the Queen has not sought to convert you to heresy?"

"Never."

"What do you talk about when you and Her Majesty are alone for so often and so long?"

"My studies, sir. My Greek, my Italian, my Hebrew; the weather, the styles."

This, they agreed later, was an unchildlike child. She was alert, amazingly wise, and intensely loyal. Though they threatened, though they shook their fingers in her face, they could not make her whimper nor could they make her change her story. Finally, exasperated, they rose.

"The Lady Jane is ordered to return to her parents at once."

"Yes, My Lords, but first I must bid Her Majesty good-by."

"You will leave at once," ordered the lord chancellor. "You are commanded not to see her again and not to let her know you have been questioned in this matter."

"But I must see her!" Jane's big eyes filled with tears now.

"It is forbidden by the King's Majesty."

"Why do you want to hurt her?" Jane cried, angry now. "She has never hurt you!"

"We are His Majesty's loyal subjects. It is our duty to see that His Majesty's laws are observed!"

When they left, Jane wanted to do nothing but fling herself on the bed and weep.

"My poor baby!" It was Mrs. Ellen, who had been listening from behind a door. "Shall we begin now to pack Your Ladyship's things?"

"I must leave her! I may never see her again! Yes, pack. I *will* see her! I don't care what they do to me!"

She started for the door.

"No, Your Ladyship! Come back! You are ordered—"

But already Jane was out the door and hurrying toward the Queen's apartments, which were not far from her own. She found the rooms empty except for one of Catherine's chamberwomen who said that the Queen was having an interview with the ambassador from Cleves. Distraught, Jane decided to wait. Let them punish her for it! She was certain that Catherine must be ignorant of what was going on. Should she warn her? After all, they had searched Jane's room once before and nothing had come of it. Besides, the King loved Catherine and depended upon her. Surely he would not have her killed!

Mrs. Ellen entered. "Come, Your Ladyship, we must go. To remain here now is to endanger yourself. Besides, if your father should hear that you had disobeyed the King's orders—"

"Go back to the packing. Order the horses. I shall not leave until I have said good-by to the Queen," replied Jane steadily.

The old woman shrugged, shook her head dolefully, and left the room.

Wriothesley, on leaving Jane, had gone directly to the King, and though he had secured no evidence, he prevailed upon the suffering monarch to sign a warrant for Catherine's arrest. This done, Wriothesley thrust the document in his doublet and hurriedly backed out of the room, hastening to his own house to summon Gardiner. They planned to make the arrest in two days.

Fortunately for Catherine, the paper slipped from its place and fell to the gallery floor, where it was found a few minutes later by one of the Queen's grooms. The man read it and gasped. The Queen! She had always been extremely kind to her servants, and he hesitated. What to do? Return the document to Wriothesley or take it to the Queen?

When Catherine finally entered the room she was smiling, but the smile faded as Jane, weeping now, ran to her.

"Why, what is it, little one?"

"Madame, you are in danger! I have been severely questioned and I am ordered to leave the palace at once."

"On whose orders? Be calm. Tell me everything."

As Jane told her about the visit of Wriothesley and his henchmen, Catherine's eyes took on a startled expression. Scarcely had the girl finished speaking when one of Her Majesty's grooms burst into the room and without ceremony thrust the warrant at her.

"Your Majesty, read this! I just found it in the gallery!"

Having shoved it into her hands, the man hastened out, frightened at what might happen to him. Catherine read the document and her face paled.

"He means to kill me!" she exclaimed. "This is a warrant for my arrest! And the King has signed it! Jane, go home. Go home quickly. Say naught about this. Pray for me, my darling!" She caught Jane to her, kissed her, and then pushed her away.

Jane was too horrified to speak. Catherine—arrested!

"Go, Jane, go!" cried Catherine.

Without the usual bow that was required by etiquette, Jane left the room, heartbroken and white-faced.

Henry VIII: Hans Holbein. Corsini Gallery, Rome

Henry VIII and his family: Princess Mary, Edward, the Queen, and Princess Elizabeth. The Queen, who should be Catherine Parr, is probably a posthumous representation of Jane Seymour, Edward's mother. Unknown artist. Hampton Court

Catherine reread the paper. There could be no doubt: She was to follow Anne Boleyn and Catherine Howard to the block. She began screaming hysterically. Her ladies came hurrying toward her.

"The Queen is ill," said Anne Herbert. "Send for the doctor at once."

They put her to bed, but they could not quiet her.

Jane's home was not far away. Her parents, hearing of their daughter's unexpected return, hastened to her sitting room. Lady Frances, her light gray eyes bright with anxiety, grabbed her daughter by the arm.

"You have displeased the King? The Queen?" she shouted shrilly.

Jane, in tears, told them nothing except that Wriothesley had interrogated her and ordered her to leave.

"I told you it was only a question of time," said Henry Grey to his wife. "Only a question of time ere Catherine Parr, too, goes to the block!"

At the word "block," Jane's tears increased.

"But we, too, are Lutherans!" said Lady Frances.

"We can change if need be," replied her husband.

For a time he stood staring thoughtfully into space—a lean, good-looking man with a long sharp nose, narrow face, and dark, cold eyes.

"Wriothesley is not our enemy," he decided at last, "and if we are pressed, we can easily deny any inclination toward that sect." He turned to his daughter, annoyed by her tears. "Stop that!" he shouted.

"If . . . if any harm should come to the Queen—" she sobbed.

He slapped her on the cheek. "That is naught to you! If she is arrested you must not defend her!"

"But I love her! I love her so!"

He slapped her again. "If she is accused, you must cease to love her. Will you never learn?" He turned irritably to Mrs.

Ellen, who had retired to the far end of the room when they entered. "What do you know of this?"

"Only what Her Ladyship has told you, sir."

"Put her to bed. Keep her there. Let no one come near her, even her sisters. Say she is ill."

When Jane had been taken to her bedroom, he turned to his wife. "Now then, what shall we do?"

"Do nothing, know nothing." Her eyes were grim. "We will not go to court today." Her voice took on its usual masterful tone. "This is one day when we remain at home. If anyone comes, we are indisposed."

While Jane was imagining Catherine a prisoner and facing the scaffold, surprising events were taking place at Whitehall. The Queen, believing that her days were numbered, continued to scream. Dr. Wendy failed to calm her.

"Her Majesty must have had some terrible shock," he declared. "There is naught I can do for her."

Henry, whose apartment was separated from his wife's only by a narrow corridor, was inconvenienced and annoyed by her cries.

"What ails the woman?" he demanded angrily.

Had Kate found out about that warrant? But how could she? He had been confined to bed for two days, and already he missed his faithful and tactful nurse. When the noise continued, he had himself hoisted into a chair and carried to her room. Catherine looked as though she were dying. Her ladies were sobbing.

"What's the matter here?" shouted the King.

"Sire," replied Dr. Wendy, "I know not what has occasioned this, but it appears the Queen has suffered some very great shock."

"Shock, eh?" Henry remembered the warrant he had signed.

How had the woman found out about it?

Catherine, hearing his voice, opened her eyes and saw him

sitting there. Her mind worked quickly. Her cries ceased. This was her opportunity to save herself. She sat up, making appealing, feminine attempts to smooth her long, beautiful hair.

"Ah, my liege, my Lord King," she said softly, and her voice assumed a beguiling tenderness, "your visit has greatly revived and rejoiced me."

His voice grew softer. "What ails you, Kate?"

She knew she must not mention the warrant, must not let him suspect that she was aware of his intention to kill her.

"I . . . I have seen so little of Your Majesty of late." She was humble and endearing as she gazed full into that bloated, oily face. "I feared I had given you some offense."

"Catherine," he admitted soberly, "there has been a plot against your life."

She opened her fine eyes wide, as though astonished.

"Be at ease, Kate," he said and grumpily signaled for his attendants to carry him out.

When he had gone, Catherine rose, knowing that she was in no danger now. "Send for Lady Jane," she said quietly. "Tell her to return."

The message filled Jane with delight. She could not reach Whitehall quickly enough.

"We have naught to fear now, my sweet," Catherine told Jane the following morning. She embraced and kissed the child. "We will not mention the warrant to anyone."

"But, Madame, how—"

"The King graciously paid me a visit last evening. Now I shall return that visit. I want you and Lady Herbert to accompany me."

A few minutes later, with Anne Herbert behind her and Jane in front carrying two candles, Catherine entered the King's bedroom. All three knelt, and then Henry motioned his wife to a chair facing his huge bed.

"Sit beside me, Kate," he said, but his eyes were cold and cunning.

Trembling, Jane put the candlesticks on a convenient table and then stood tensely beside Anne Herbert, her eyes on Catherine, who seemed quite calm and trustful. "Oh, be careful, Madame!" she was pleading silently. "Be careful!"

But Catherine meant to be careful. Apparently relaxed, she listened intently while Henry adroitly began to talk about religion. She listened, nodding from time to time, her eyes bright with interest. She knew he was trying to trap her into another theological argument, but the time for such things had passed. She had learned a lesson. Never again would she contradict her husband.

"Well, Kate," he asked at last, "have you no answer to that?"

"Sire," she replied, her eyes modestly downcast, "I am but a woman, having all the imperfections of my sex, therefore in matters of doubt and difficulty I must refer myself to Your Majesty's better judgment. You are my lord and head, for so has God appointed you. You are the supreme head of us all and, next to God, I would learn of you."

"Not so, by St. Mary! You are become a doctor, Kate, to instruct me and not to be instructed by me."

"Indeed, if Your Majesty has so conceived, my meaning has been mistaken, for I have always held it preposterous for a woman to instruct her lord. If I have ever presumed to differ with Your Highness on religion, it was partly to obtain instruction regarding certain points on which I stood in doubt, and sometimes it was because I perceived that, in talking, you were better able to pass away the pain and weariness of your present infirmity."

He smiled, a broad and normal smile. The piglike eyes became fond. "Is it so, sweetheart? Then we are perfect friends." He drew her to him, kissing her.

Jane sighed with relief. Conversation after that became

general and genial, and when at last the three ladies left they knew that Catherine, by her tact, was—at least for the present—in no danger.

Next day, the day set for the Queen's arrest, Wriothesley, followed by forty guardsmen, arrived at Whitehall to take her into custody. True, the paper with the King's signature had been lost, but he meant to arrest the woman anyhow. To his dismay, he found her on the terrace that overlooked the Thames. It was a placid, happy family group, with Catherine seated beside the King, smiling and calm, Jane leaning on the arm of her chair, and Anne Herbert standing nearby.

At sight of the lord chancellor, Henry flew into one of his rages. "Beast! Fool! Knave!" he shouted. "Get out of here!"

"Sire," begged Catherine, "do not excite yourself. Let me plead for the lord chancellor. Whatever he has done, I am sure it was only a mistake."

"Little do you know, Kate, how this man is undeserving of your goodness. On my word, sweetheart, he has been to you a very knave!"

"Whatever his offense, sire, I beg you to overlook it."

At that moment she possessed the power to have Wriothesley and Gardiner killed, as they had hoped to have her killed, but through her influence the lord chancellor and the Bishop of Winchester were permitted to remain free men.

"Wonderful, wonderful Catherine!" thought Jane. "Oh, when I grow up, may I be just like you!"

In late 1545 Jane had to leave her beloved Catherine for some months because her grandfather, the notorious Charles Brandon, Duke of Suffolk, was dying. Lady Frances and her two eldest daughters went to stay with him at Tilsey: not that she loved her father, but she knew that by showing him this attention he would bequeath her a large inheritance. She was not disappointed.

After the funeral, Jane, in deep mourning, returned to Catherine at Westminster.

Toward the end of 1546, Henry took a sharp turn for the worse. It was illegal to predict the death of the King, so it was impossible even to tell him that he was dying. By October he could not get out of bed and his hands were so puffy that he could scarcely put his signature to state papers. But his mind remained clear. By November he could not even sit up in bed. He snarled, he fumed, he complained.

Though he was not ready to die, he decided in late December to make a will, primarily to settle the matter of succession. The will, secret until after his death, decreed that the crown should go to Edward.

In the event that Edward should die without issue (children), the crown was to go to Mary. At Mary's death without issue, it was to be Elizabeth's. Should Elizabeth die without issue, the crown was to go to Jane; and if she should die, to her sisters, Catherine and Mary Grey. Anyone who dared to alter this will was to be deemed a traitor and beheaded. There was another girl who had a claim equal to Jane's: Mary of Scotland, granddaughter of the King's sister Margaret, but he did not mention her. Nor did he mention Lady Frances, who, one would think, would rightly precede her daughters.

The will named a Council of Regency to control state affairs until Edward should come of age, when he should rule in his own right. No one was given precedence in the council because Henry trusted no man with supreme power. However, one of the first acts of the council after Henry's death was to name Edward Seymour as Protector of the King and of the realm. The two Seymour brothers, Edward and Thomas, had been rising steadily in power ever since their sister Jane had married the King back in 1536—and given him his only male heir. Now they were to be elevated even higher, for Thomas had also been named a member of the Council of Regency.

In the anterooms and corridors of Westminster Palace the courtiers waited anxiously. Pages and grooms moved softly and spoke in whispers.

It seemed incredible that King Henry was dying. He lay there in an enormous bed hung with crimson velvet and cloth of gold, in a vast room furnished sumptuously with carved oak furniture upholstered in Florentine brocade, its walls covered by Flemish tapestries. From this room the courtiers came and went, assuming an air of lightness while waiting for that stupendous man to die, but half assured that he wouldn't. Not Henry. He would outtrick death itself. Though he was not yet fifty-six, his hair was now white. His gray eyes glittering, he was still signing death warrants, groaning, swearing, thundering out commands.

Four days before the end he surprised everyone by sending for Princess Mary. They did not talk long, but she said later that he had not mentioned Elizabeth. He simply ordered her to take care of Edward.

Knowing that he could not last much longer, she remained in the palace, keeping to her own apartment, holding her rosary. Jane would often come to her there, but they had little to say to each other now and often sat for hours in silence, hand in hand.

The day before Henry died, Catherine had spent many hours with him, worn out with nursing, yet trying to appear bright and untroubled, humoring and pacifying him. He was beyond the need for massaging and poulticing. When night came she, Mary, and Jane, fatigued by the strain, retired early.

Standing around the deathbed were Edward and Thomas Seymour with several other gentlemen of the court, as well as Doctors Wendy, Owen, and Gale.

The eyes of the King were staring into space as though watching something only he could see. Several times he was heard to mutter "Nan Boleyn" as though she were there at the foot of his bed. Then, again and again, he whispered "Monks, monks." It was as though he were watching an endless parade of the hundreds of priests he had murdered.

On Thursday, between one and two in the morning of January 28, 1547, Henry Tudor was pronounced dead.

By four o'clock that morning, Edward and Thomas Seymour were galloping to Hertford. They arrived at daybreak and sent an attendant to awaken Edward, now King Edward VI. The following Monday, on January 31 at three in the afternoon, he would enter London as king. But Edward Seymour, soon to be made Lord Protector and regent, was the most powerful man in England.

And Catherine Parr was free at last.

The Seymours

Despite the fact that members of Henry's court had been expecting his death, when it actually happened it was a shock. They could not believe that that roaring, self-centered, browbeating tyrant was really gone.

But adjustments were swiftly made.

First there was the entrance of Edward VI into London and the hearty cries of "Long live the King!" There was nothing of his father in Edward. The new King, not yet ten, was sensitive, studious, somewhat sickly. In accord with custom, he entered London with enormous fanfare and was taken to the royal apartments in the Tower, where he was to stay in seclusion until the coronation.

The day after King Henry's death Jane had been sent home, for Catherine, now Queen Dowager, was faced with the necessity of settling in a new establishment and adjusting herself to new conditions. She had expected that Henry would appoint her as regent, but he had not done so.

In Parliament Sir William Paget, secretary of state, read Henry's will. Lady Frances was incensed when she learned its contents. Why had her uncle ignored *her* in regard to the succession? It was she and not her daughter who should rightfully have been named third in line after Edward. But no; he had given this honor to Jane, and consequently it was Jane who bore the brunt of her resentment.

At Henry's funeral, though women were not permitted to attend the rites for a man, Catherine, Mary, Bess, Jane, Lady Frances, and other noble ladies, all garbed in deepest mourning, were permitted to hear Cranmer's oration from a closet-like alcove and to pray for the King's soul.

Bess, not yet fourteen, was as vivacious as ever, and her reddish hair had been made even redder by the use of henna. Mary, who was becoming increasingly a fanatic, felt an alien among these Protestants, and determined to leave London as soon as possible and live a secluded life. She would have died rather than renounce her religion, though even now everyone seemed determined to force her to relinquish the faith that was her sole source of comfort. Edward had tried. Edward Seymour and his wife had subtly threatened, but Mary remained firm. As first in line to the throne, she was now accorded all outward respect, but she trusted no one but Jane and her sister Catherine—not even Bess any longer.

On February 16, after the long dirges and eulogies, Henry was buried in St. George's Chapel at Windsor, and the royal ladies separated. Elizabeth, with her own officers and ladies, was to live under the care of Queen Dowager Catherine, who had been given the manor house in Chelsea—a delightful dwelling on the Thames, with small turrets, crenelated battlements, and long, high windows. The grounds included a fishpond and beautiful gardens surrounded by a high wall.

On February 19, Edward, riding a white horse under a white silk canopy edged with silver, rode in a procession from the Tower to Westminster. He was garbed in silver cloth, with a flowing cloak of silver edged with pearls. To most people he was an ordinary-looking boy, but to Jane he seemed a most splendid prince. On one side of him rode Edward Seymour, on the other side Thomas Seymour, and the three were followed by Archbishop Cranmer and a long line of gorgeously clad nobles, including Henry and Frances Grey and their two elder daughters. They passed through streets hung with cloth of gold. While trumpets blared, the people of London saw their new king and cried out their blessings upon him.

Reaching Westminster, where Edward was to stay until his coronation, there was a banquet from which the women were excluded. The following day came the coronation. After this there were jousts, but Jane, seated in a box with her mother and the Queen Dowager, scarcely watched the games at all.

Her eyes were fixed adoringly upon Edward, who seemed to her the embodiment of all that was manly, all that was good. She could not approach him and tell him so, but several times their eyes met and he smiled at her with a grin that made her feel happily close to him. Her Edward, her King—her dear friend.

Once the ceremonies were ended, Edward Seymour worked quickly. One of his first steps was to be named Protector by the Council of the Realm, and then to persuade the boy king to create him the Duke of Somerset. In his new role he would need supporters, and he secured elevations in rank for other nobles who might aid him: Wriothesley was made Earl of Southampton; Sir Thomas Seymour became Baron Seymour of Sudeley and lord high admiral; John Dudley, Viscount Lisle, was created the Earl of Warwick. The ceremony lasted from seven in the morning until noon, and at its conclusion the young King fainted.

Among Edward Seymour's plans was that the proposed marriage between King Edward and the young Queen of Scots should come to nothing, and eventually the King would marry Anne Seymour, his daughter, while Jane Grey would marry his son Edward, the Earl of Hertford, then a boy of about seven.

But Thomas Seymour had other plans. Thomas hoped eventually to supersede his brother, to be named regent, to secure control over the King. One way to become more powerful would be to marry either Mary or Bess. Soon after King Henry's funeral he offered his hand to each of them in turn and was rejected. This did not depress him. His next move was to try to bring about a marriage between Jane Grey and King Edward. He sent his man of affairs, William Sharington, to discuss the possibility of Jane's coming to live with him and his mother at Seymour House in London. Jane's parents were astonished at such a proposal. At first they demurred, puzzled as to what lay behind this surprising suggestion.

Sharington smoothly assured Henry Grey of Lord Thomas' abiding friendship. "It would be a goodly thing," he went on, "if your daughter, the Lady Jane, were in the keeping of the lord admiral. I have often heard him say that the Lady Jane was the handsomest lady in England and that he would see her placed in marriage much to your comfort, sir."

"With whom would he match her?" asked Henry Grey guardedly, for he and his wife had already agreed that it would be to their advantage if Jane were to marry the son of the Protector.

"I doubt not but that you shall see her married to the King."

"What! The King! But—"

"Have no fear. Lord Thomas will bring this about."

When Sharington had gone, Henry and Lady Frances discussed the proposal at great length. As a match for Jane, the King was certainly preferable to young Seymour. Still, they did not intend to offend the Protector. In the end, Henry decided to go to Seymour House next day and have a private talk with Thomas.

At this same time Jane paid a visit to Chelsea Manor. Only Elizabeth was there, for Catherine had gone to see her stepson, much to the Protector's displeasure. Knowing King Edward's fondness for the Queen Dowager, Somerset was determined to keep them apart as much as possible. Catherine, in turn, disliked and distrusted Edward Seymour. She especially abhorred his wife, Anne, a venomous, tart-tongued woman who, now that her husband held the exalted post of Protector, had assumed increasingly royal airs.

Jane and Bess, who had been forced to greet each other formally at the funeral, now met without ceremony, since no one was present but the two Mrs. Ashleys, who kept some distance away, leaving the girls practically alone.

Bess had not changed much since those early days at Hunsdon. Though short, she had a good figure, and her dark eyes, making an attractive contrast to her red hair, were more animated than ever. Catherine had always affectionately referred to her as "our Eliza," and Jane used that name now.

"Is our Eliza glad to be living with the Queen?" she said.

"Yes. I'm quite fond of Catherine. I hear that your parents are among Edward Seymour's stanchest supporters. I couldn't say this to anyone but you, but I detest that man and his vixenish wife. In fact, I dislike all the Seymours except Lord Thomas. Listen, I'll tell you a secret. I've had my first proposal!"

"Oh? Who?"

"None other than Lord Thomas, the lord admiral! Will you believe it? No sooner was my father dead than he offered me his hand!"

"You . . . you didn't—"

"I admit I find the man attractive, but having thought it over I decided it was wise not to become involved with any branch of that family."

"But I thought he was in love with Lady Catherine!"

Elizabeth's eyes grew hard. "Love! The man is a schemer. He wants to become regent and supplant his brother. He wants power. As for Catherine—after all, she is the Queen Dowager and an extremely wealthy woman. Are you naïve enough to imagine that Thomas was in love with her? No, not wholly. Besides, that was a long time ago. I am second in line to the throne. I daresay he considered that. I admit I find the rogue fascinating. Most ladies do, it seems, but . . ."

"But he's so much older than you."

"Yet he seems young. No, Jane, I doubt that he loves me for myself. He hates his brother, and to wed an heiress to the throne—can you imagine how that would displease the all-powerful Duke of Somerset? Oh, I know my world, Jane! We must move carefully in it. All of us are under the whip of the Protector now. But let's change the subject. Let's talk about styles. This new-fashioned collar becomes me, don't you think?"

Trusting Jane, Bess chattered on freely. It was amazing, Jane thought, how much Bess knew about what was going on. She knew, for instance, that King Edward had once been fond of Jane, calling her his "sweet sister," but also that Edward Seymour, now that he was in control, meant to alienate the two young people. When Bess had asked permission to call upon the King, the Duke of Somerset had replied that an interview was "not convenient."

"So I'm to be kept away from my brother, you see."

"Why? What motive could Somerset have?"

"Don't you see? He wishes to hold Edward and will not chance any control but his own. Somerset would like to exclude Catherine and Lord Thomas if possible—and you, too! Poor Edward! If he were fond of Somerset it would be different, but he dislikes the man as much as I do. Heaven help England now that Edward Seymour rules it! Suddenly it is dangerous to hurt him."

When Jane left Chelsea Manor she had much to think about.

Did Thomas Seymour love Bess or did he still care for Catherine? And how far would it go, this feud between him and his brother? She recalled how her parents fawned upon the Duke of Somerset now, just as they had once fawned upon King Henry. She, too, had written asking for a private audience with the King and had received the same reply, signed by Somerset, as Bess had. Was she never to be permitted to see her old playmate?

Arriving home, she was surprised to see her parents obviously awaiting her in the great hall of Durham House, their new mansion.

"I have just returned from having a long talk with Lord Thomas," her father told her frigidly.

When Henry Grey, the wealthy Marquess of Dorset, had had the opportunity to marry Lady Frances Brandon, daughter of the Duke of Suffolk and niece of King Henry, he had not hesitated for a moment, for such a union would advance his position at court. Unfeelingly he had thrown over the sister of the Earl of Arundel, to whom he had been troth-plighted at the time. One would have thought that he had enough of worldly goods, for he owned many castles and estates in Leicestershire. But he was an ambitious man, eager to be of service to the King. He and Lady Frances had now been married for thirteen years, and despite the fact that they had three daughters, they had never pretended to be in love. Love was an emotion utterly foreign to both of them. Henry Grey had no affection even for his children. His entire concern regarding them was to find advantageous alliances for them and by this means form connections between himself and other rich and powerful families. Just as, thirteen years earlier, he had discarded the girl who loved him, so now he was ready to sacrifice his daughter to the same ends.

"Did you hear me?" he repeated impatiently. "I said I had just had a long talk with the lord admiral."

"But what has that to do with me, Your Grace?" asked Jane.

"Tomorrow you are to go and live under his care," announced Lady Frances. "His house is run by his mother, who will look after you. Henceforth you are to regard Lord Thomas as your guardian."

"But why?"

Always tense, Lady Frances swept toward Jane and gave her a slap on the cheek. "It is not for you to question your parents. You will do as you are told. Lord Thomas is now your foster father."

"Yes, Madame."

Though puzzled as to why Thomas should want to take her under his care, Jane was glad to be going to live in his home. She was so badly treated by her parents that she was always eager to go anywhere she would be free from their slappings and pinches and scoldings. But why would Lord Thomas want to be her guardian?

Next morning, accompanied by her usual retinue—two footmen, two maids, Mrs. Ashley, and Mrs. Ellen—she arrived at Seymour House, to be greeted by Thomas' widowed mother, the Dowager Lady Seymour, who, though she was King Edward's grandmother, had always kept aloof from court.

Still wondering why she was there, Jane asked no questions. The Dowager Lady, who seemed to have reached an age where she was not surprised at anything, gave no explanation. The lord admiral was almost never at home, and when Jane chanced to meet him in the hall, he passed by with no more than a gay nod. His aged mother, though she treated Jane kindly, was reserved and cold, leaving the girl entirely alone.

Thomas Seymour's elder brother and his wife, the Duke and Duchess of Somerset, were filled with indignation and suspicion when they learned that Thomas had made himself Jane's guardian. They had always been friendly with the Greys. Their son and daughter had frequently been guests at Bradgate, the Greys' country estate in Leicestershire, and the Greys had seemed flatteringly receptive to the idea of Jane's marriage with their son Edward, Earl of Hertford. And now, with the consent of her parents, she was under

Group at Henry VIII's deathbed, showing Edward VI
enthroned behind him, attended by members of
his Privy Council: Unknown artist

ABOVE: Charles Brandon, Duke of Suffolk,
Jane Grey's grandfather: Unknown artist

RIGHT: Edward Seymour, Duke of Somerset,
uncle and Protector of Edward VI: Unknown artist

Thomas Seymour, Baron Seymour of Sudeley,
uncle of Edward VI: Unknown artist

the control of the debonair, fascinating Thomas. Why? As-tute as they were, they could not fathom his motive, and the Greys gave no satisfactory explanation.

For the present, however, the Somersets strove to conceal their chagrin. In the Council of Regency there was still talk of a marriage between King Edward and Mary Stuart, Queen of Scots, though Somerset had decided that this would never materialize. He was a wise and wily man. His youngest daughter, Anne Seymour, pretty and accomplished, was often taken to visit the King. Knowing Edward's fondness for Jane Grey, Somerset had determined that she and Edward should see as little as possible of each other, and so when Jane wrote again and again asking for permission to see her beloved playfellow, her requests were politely refused, nor was she permitted to attend any state functions at Edward's court.

Had the Somersets known what was to be Thomas' next move, they might have been even more annoyed. Night after night would find him, carefully avoiding being seen, knock-ing at the postern gate at Chelsea Manor to plead his great love for Catherine and implore her to marry him at once.

Catherine, who had never ceased to love him, happily agreed, but it was necessary to get the King's consent. The poor young King was kept in a constant state of turmoil, what with Thomas trying to poison his mind against Somerset and Somerset trying to keep him away from Thomas. Since it was impossible for Somerset to prevent Catherine from seeing Edward sometimes, she and Thomas man-aged one day to visit the boy and secure his approval of the match in writing. He freely gave his permission and agreed that he would not tell Somerset of the marriage until Catherine herself chose to announce it.

Since Henry had died in late January, good taste dictated that Catherine wait at least six months before remarriage, but she and Thomas were secretly married in May. Soon after this, Catherine called at Seymour House to see Jane. They had not met since Henry's funeral and now they rushed joyously into each other's arms.

"Jane," began Catherine, after dismissing Mrs. Ellen and Mrs. Ashley, "we shall soon be together again, and this time forever!"

"Nothing could make me happier, Madame."

"You must promise not to mention this. Even our Eliza doesn't know about it yet, but I am the wife of Thomas Seymour!"

Jane gasped.

"I shall announce it in June," Catherine continued blissfully.

"Oh!" Jane wondered if Catherine knew that Thomas had previously proposed to Mary and to Bess, but she wisely did not mention this. Catherine was radiant with joy. She seemed much younger than her thirty-five years and even more beautiful than when Jane had first seen her. "May you be happy, Madame."

"I am sure we shall be."

"The Protector will be displeased."

"Oh, assuredly; but we have the King's approval. So be prepared to move to Chelsea soon. We shall be a real family there. You have always been like my own daughter, darling, and now you will live with me forever. Oh, Jane, in all my life I have never been happier!"

"And Edward is pleased? Oh, if only I could see him! I have written again and again but—"

"His mail is watched by the Protector. He probably never received the letters. But the last time I saw him we talked of you and he wants to see you. Trust me; I'll arrange a meeting. The Protector sees to it that the King is rarely left alone, but there are people close to him who can be bribed. The Protector gives Edward no money, you know, but he manages to send letters to Thomas, all hastily scribbled on wrapping paper and asking for money. If Thomas and I were his protectors, the dear lad would be delighted. We understand him, we love him. Perhaps someday—but I won't go into that. I must go now. Mind you keep my secret!"

"I promise. Oh, how happy I shall be, living with you!"

They parted affectionately and, true to her word, Catherine managed to secure permission for Jane to visit Edward a few days later.

The girl entered the room to find the King surrounded by gentlemen in waiting. Since these elders were present, the two friends assumed a tone of formality. Jane murmured "Your Majesty" and sank to her knees. Edward bowed, his young face impassive. Their words were impersonal. Jane hoped the King's Grace was well and wished him a long and happy reign. He replied stolidly. At last, displaying a flare of temper comparable to his father's, he ordered his gentlemen out of the room. Once the boy and girl were alone, he reached out both hands to her, smiling in the old fond and friendly way.

"Jane, Jane, how I've wanted to see you!"

"And I've wanted to see Your Majesty."

"No, no, when we're alone don't call me that. I'm still Edward, your friend, always your friend. To you I can really talk—and oh, Jane, I need someone to talk to!"

"Did you get my letters? I've written often."

"No, I had none of them. I wondered why you didn't answer mine. It seems so long since I've seen you!"

"You've grown much taller." She gazed at him as though he were the most handsome youth in the world; and to her, he was. "Do you remember how we used to roll hoops together at Hunsdon?"

"Yes, and ride hobbyhorses. And I remember the time you brought those French wooden dolls and made me play that I was their father and you were my wife. How happy we were then!"

"Aren't you happy now, Edward?"

His sad, dark eyes grew bright with torment. "Happy! I'm miserable. I am called king, yet I have no power. I don't like my Uncle Edward. He gives me no money. He permits me to see only those whom he wants me to see. I know that he is not a fit man to rule. I worry about the country. I know the people detest him. He's constantly trying to turn me against the Queen, against Uncle Thomas and Mary and Bess. And I have eight years to go before I can be free of him!"

"The people love you, Edward. They're depending on you. They're waiting hopefully until the time when you will govern."

Her words had no cheering effect. He sighed. "Meanwhile, I must put up with Uncle Edward. You know, don't you, Jane, that shortly before my father died he urged the nobles to carry out the agreement with Scotland that provides for my marriage to its queen?"

She nodded, her eyes pained, for suddenly the thought of Edward's marriage was disturbing.

"But I doubt that it will take place," he continued.

"Yet of course you must marry, Edward."

"Yes; but as for the Scottish marriage, Uncle Edward has no notion of obeying my father's wishes. He's determined that I shall marry his daughter!"

"What! Anne Seymour?"

"Yes."

"By my faith!" It took several minutes for Jane to accept this. After a pause she added generously, "She is very pretty and very learned."

"I won't marry her! He'll never make me! He forces me to do many things, but never that! Oh, it hasn't yet been openly suggested, but I'm not blind nor a fool. She's my cousin and I don't dislike her. I thing she's quite nice, but I won't marry her."

"No, Edward," she said soothingly. "Marry where your heart is."

"There you speak like an idiot!" he replied bitterly. "I cannot expect to do that and neither can you. You'll have to marry in accord with your parents' wishes, but I have no parents. I intend to marry for the good of the country. I have certain duties. I cannot expect to live like people who are non-royal. Oh, why did the council make Edward Seymour the Protector? If only I could be free of him! And yet I can't. There's no way. He governs the council. They are all his henchmen."

"Your father had great regard for Edward Seymour. Even before your mother married the King, Edward was in His Majesty's service. I remember hearing it said that when my grandmother went to France to marry its king, Edward Seymour was in her train."

"Despite his long service, I tell you, Jane, he's not fit to rule. He cares nothing about the people. He thinks only of himself and his own aggrandizement. I remember when he came to Hertford where Bess and I were then living to tell us that my father was dead, I had the feeling that the man was somehow like a toad. I don't trust him, Jane. It would be better if Uncle Thomas were the Protector."

"Lord Thomas is my guardian now. I suppose you know that. I don't know why my father turned me over to him. Do you?"

"No. It seems to me that grownups do many incomprehensible things. Uncle Thomas is generous and gay. I'm fond of him, but in my heart I don't quite trust him, either. Why would he want to assume guardianship of you? He . . . wait now! I have it! Why didn't I realize it before? It is because you are third in line for the succession! And there's something else. I remember the way he spoke about you yesterday. Jane, he hopes to promote a marriage between us!"

"Between you and me?" Jane was shocked. "Oh, no Edward! You must be mistaken!"

"No, I'm not, Jane. It is all clear to me now. Ho, here's an odd situation! One uncle tries to bring about a marriage between me and his daughter, and the other uncle hopes to promote a marriage between me and his ward!"

"You and I—married? No, that couldn't be!"

He sat close to her and took her hand, speaking gently. "No, Jane, it cannot be, and I wish you to understand why. It is not that I don't love you or trust you, but I know that the treasury is almost empty. Somerset is spending the money on himself and his favorites while the people starve! By the time I really become king, England will be bankrupt. So I must marry a foreign princess who will bring much gold into the country. I must form some strong alliance, for under Edward Seymour the realm grows weak. Do you understand, Jane?"

She nodded, troubled, not knowing what to say.

Should she mention Catherine's wedding? Should she tell Edward how Lord Thomas had first proposed to Mary and then to Bess? She decided not to speak of that.

"Jane," he begged, still holding her hand, "come to see me often. I need someone to whom I can talk freely like this. I truly trust you—you and my venerated mother, Catherine. You two in all the world."

"Not Mary? Not Bess?"

"Bess thinks mainly of herself. As for Mary, she's wrapped up in her religion. Do you realize, Jane, that the kingdom is full of people who still celebrate the Mass secretly and carry hidden rosaries? Abomination!"

She was astonished at his vehemence and saw that Edward had grown as bigoted about Protestantism as Mary was about Catholicism. This prejudice had come about through Edward Seymour's influence. Not that Seymour and those who surrounded him, including her own parents, were sincere religionists, but they had grown rich on the spoils from the monasteries and knew that if Catholicism should be re-established they would be forced to give up many of their properties.

"Edward," she said gently, "I'm sure it's wise to let people worship in their own way."

He released her hand and drew away from her. "How can you say such a thing? When I rule I shall stamp out that religion! I shall—"

"Please, Edward, don't let this excite you so. It—"

There was a knock on the door. Edward gave an exasperated sigh. "Enter!"

A groom opened the door and knelt. "His Majesty's tutor has arrived."

"Yes." Edward turned to Jane, his tone formal. "I hope the Lady Jane will visit me again—soon."

She rose, knelt. "As soon as I am permitted to do so, Your Majesty. Tomorrow I am going to visit the Princess Mary at Newhall for a month. When I return, sire, if you will permit me—"

The formality that they must observe when they were not alone infuriated him.

"Come as often as you can!" he cried angrily.

She smiled, still kneeling. "It is a command, my liege?"

"Yes!"

She rose and backed toward the door, an elegant little figure in a simple velvet gown with a high collar flaring outward in the back and long ropes of pearls reaching below her tiny waist. For the first time Edward noticed how graceful she was, what a lovely smile she had, and how long her eyelashes were. When she reached the door he was tempted to order her to stay, but—since the groom's back was to her —she waved at him cheerily and was gone.

Once in the corridor, Jane's bright smile faded. Could it be true that Lord Thomas was determined that she and Edward should marry? If he wished it, Catherine must wish it, too! But how could they possibly accomplish this so long as Edward Seymour was in power? Did they hope between them to overthrow him? Wisely, she decided not to mention the subject to anyone.

Chelsea Manor

Arriving at Seymour House, Jane found that her maids had finished packing for the journey to Newhall. Since Mary was now first in line to the succession, all the nobles considered it politic to visit her, and Jane knew that her father would accompany her.

It was an impressive cavalcade that started toward Newhall next morning, including over a hundred men-at-arms, maids, tutors, valets. Jane and her father rode on richly caparisoned horses with beplumed heads and long, flowing tails.

Henry Grey and his daughter rarely spoke. Jane thought, when occasionally she glanced at him, that he looked every inch the aristocrat. His long, thin face was grave. His full mustache had been stiffly waxed, and his short, full chin beard was lustrous with the consistent use of fragrant oil. She wondered if he knew of the lord admiral's plan to marry her to the King, but then she realized that he must know, else he would never have agreed that she should be Lord Thomas' ward. Then she told herself that Edward might be mistaken. How pleasant it would be if she could turn to her father and talk the whole thing over frankly! But never had he caressed her, never had he encouraged her to confide in him.

After a long silence he ordered her to sit straighter in the saddle and to hold the reins lower. Then they rode for miles without even looking at each other. Jane had much to think about—Edward, his unhappiness, the clear evidence of bigotry she had seen in him. This, however, was his only fault. Edward, to her, was handsome and dear, but to dream of marrying him seemed preposterous.

The thought of being queen—even queen consort—was unappealing, even alarming. If he had been plain Edward Tudor—but no, he was her sovereign and her friend and could never be anything else. She thought of Mary and found it distasteful to imagine prim, homely Mary ever being queen, for Mary would show no mercy to anyone who did not profess her own beliefs. But Mary would never rule, for Edward would marry some foreign princess and have children. Edward would make a fine king.

In imagination Jane could see Mary Tudor, who was now awaiting them at Newhall and probably not overjoyed at the thought of their arrival: a short-necked, intelligent woman, holding herself ramrod straight; a good musician; a person who felt herself to be unloved and who seemingly loved no one. Henry Grey, too, was obviously thinking of Mary, for suddenly, out of a deep silence, he became loquacious.

"I remember her mother, Catherine of Aragon; a fine woman, saintly, gracious, stately. Never did she show bitterness, despite the fact that Henry treated her shamefully. Of his six wives, she was the only one who truly loved him."

"Did my father speak in her defense?"

"I? I'm not a fool." He was annoyed by the question. "But I remember how she loved Mary and how fondly she used to teach the child Latin. I remember their anguish when Henry separated them. Mary was rather pretty as a child, and before the divorce I think Henry was fond of her. But she made the mistake of siding with her beloved mother. Well, that is all in the past. She is wise to live a retired life. Heaven help England if she ever becomes queen!" He gazed about guiltily to make sure none of the grooms was within hearing distance.

"Why?"

"We shall all have to become papists. Everyone knows that she still celebrates Mass. In this she defies Somerset and the council. She seems to like you. Encourage her in this if you can, for one never knows. Only he who agrees with the one in power is ever safe."

Jane did not answer. Such a philosophy was abhorrent to her. How sad that in order to stay alive and free one must echo such a person as Edward Seymour!

When at last they arrived at Newhall, Mary greeted them graciously, though she was suffering from a cold. It seemed to Jane that Mary was always suffering either from a cold or a headache. Henry Grey remained for only a few days and then left for London. With his going, Mary became more relaxed, spending as much time as possible with Jane and talking less guardedly.

As usual, she asked questions. Was it true that Edward was practically a prisoner? That Catherine and the Duchess of Somerset were constantly at loggerheads? That Thomas Seymour had become Jane's guardian? That her parents had decided to espouse her to Somerset's son, the Earl of Hertford? Did she like the boy? Was Bess happy, living with Catherine?

Mary, who was living in luxury by this time, gave Jane a magnificent gold necklace set with pearls.

"It becomes you, Jane," she said in her sober way, her dark eyes brooding. "You'll be really beautiful when you grow up, but always remember that outer beauty is a minor and fleeting thing. I hope you will never become vain like Bess."

"I? Beautiful? With these freckles? Oh, but the necklace is lovely, Mary! Thank you."

Mary dismissed her thanks with a wave of the hand. "Let us talk of more important things."

Mary's "more important things" consisted in doing her duty. And she considered it her duty to convert the girl to what she was convinced was the only true faith. She argued intelligently, lengthily, patiently, though it was evident that she was only making her guest uncomfortable. By the time Jane left for London, Mary's farewells were cold, even resentful, and Jane felt that never again would their friendship be as close as it had been in the past. She understood Mary, respected her, and was sincerely grieved at the change in their relationship.

Nothing had altered at Seymour House except that the old Dowager Lady Seymour was more silent than ever, secretly troubled about the feud between her two sons. Jane had not been back in London long before she learned of the increased enmity between Catherine and the Duchess of Somerset.

This placed the nobles in an unpleasant predicament, for they must be careful not to take sides, though they disliked the duchess, who had come to be secretly named "the scorpion," and considered that Catherine was in the right. Everyone knew that just as Somerset had always been jealous of his brother, the duchess had always been jealous of Catherine.

But Jane was so busy with her studies that she had scant time to think of such things. Her tutor, Roger Ascham, was also the tutor of Elizabeth, and though he considered Bess an outstanding pupil, he made no secret of the fact that Jane was a prodigy. Her aptitude for learning amazed him. This noted Greek scholar and author had other pupils besides the two royal ladies, for he also taught at Cambridge, but Jane was certainly his prize student. It had become the fashion among court ladies to consider learning important. All studied Greek, and Elizabeth began each day with an hour's reading of the Greek Testament. Most of these women were disagreeably boastful about their proficiency, but Jane remained simple in her tastes, modest and unspoiled in her manners, and never fully satisfied with her progress. She was fond of Ascham, looked forward to her hours of study with him, and always tried to please him.

He, on the other hand, found it delightful to work with so brilliant a student and was unstinting in his praise of her.

A week after her return to Seymour House, accompanied by eight men-at-arms, she decided to visit Catherine. The Queen Dowager was alone in the garden—and what a lovely, tranquil garden it was! The two, both still dressed in black in mourning for King Henry, sat close together near the fishpond.

Catherine looked radiant, and no one would have guessed her true age. Her first questions had to do with Jane's lessons, for she always considered these of prime importance. After a while Jane brought the conversation around to Edward. Had Catherine seen him lately?

"Yes," said Catherine. "Ah, poor boy! More and more he detests Somerset, but perhaps ere long we shall remedy that."

"How?"

"We will find a way, never fear. He's extremely fond of Lord Thomas, you know."

"Yes, and speaking of Lord Thomas, surely, Madame, you won't be able to keep your marriage a secret much longer?"

"We don't intend to. Every night when weather permits, I admit him into my garden by that little postern gate. Even our Eliza doesn't suspect."

"Madame, tell me truly. Do you and Lord Thomas hope to have Somerset deposed and become protectors of Edward and the realm?"

"Exactly. But you mustn't breathe a word of this to anyone."

"I hope it will happen. Edward would be much more at ease under your charge. But how could such a thing take place?"

"It is not impossible. Thomas is popular with the people. Somerset is unpopular. Besides, you are right about Edward's being happier—yes, and healthier—if he were in our care."

"My dearest Lady!" Jane gazed at her adoringly. "When shall I come here to live with you?"

"Soon, my sweet. We'll all be so happy! I think perhaps you don't know that Thomas and I have been in love for a long time, even before I married the King. Oh, he's madly in love with me, Jane! I hope someday you may know such a love. I was Henry's wife for three years, six months, and fourteen days—years of bondage. I had married twice before, but never for love. And now at last love, real love, has come to me! Strange that I should be saying all this to one as young as you, but you've always seemed much older than you are. I suppose that's because you have always lived among adults. And what an example these people have set for you! All of them intent only upon acquiring power and prestige. Yet you, my darling Jane, remain beautifully uncontaminated. But speaking about the Protector—his power will soon wane. There are many who eye him enviously and are eager to destroy him, just as he is certain to destroy anyone whom he suspects of trying to forge ahead of him."

Jane nodded, knowing that chief among those was Lord Thomas Seymour. She wondered if he really loved Catherine as much as he pretended, or if his true reason for marrying her was because such a union would strengthen his position. But she tried to dismiss this thought. Who wouldn't love Catherine for herself? Catherine, who was all that was lovable, loving, and lovely?

"I suppose you know how the Duchess of Somerset, in her spite, has done everything she can to annoy me?" went on Catherine, her fine eyes now flashing angrily. "Would you believe it, Somerset, trying to hurt me, has declared that all the jewels Henry gave me as gifts actually belong to the crown?"

"Oh, no! How despicable!"

"Yes, despicable! And just yesterday he showed his power by taking them away from me! Well, tomorrow Thomas and

I will announce our marriage. What chagrin that will cause Somerset and his venomous wife!"

Catherine was right. With the announcement of her marriage to Lord Thomas, the enmity of the duchess became even more blatant. Had she and her husband suspected that such a union was being considered, they would have done their utmost to prevent it. But Catherine and Thomas had kept their secret well.

What further infuriated the Somersets was the King's continued fondness for his "dearest mother" and his Uncle Thomas. Well, the Somersets would bide their time, determined that ultimately they would find a way to remove this threat to their position.

The hate and vindictiveness of the Somersets apparently had no effect upon the happiness of the newlyweds. To them the future seemed full of promise. They would gain control of the King; they would marry him to Jane, who adored him. It would be a perfect marriage. Jane and Edward seemed to belong together. But first they must manage somehow to depose Somerset.

On the day Jane left Seymour House for Chelsea Manor she made no attempt to mask her joy. To live with Catherine forever! She wanted to run to Edward and tell him about it, but this was impossible. Edward was Somerset's captive.

After arriving at Chelsea, Jane began to be really acquainted with her charming guardian. Thomas Seymour was certainly a vivid personality and a delightful companion. He was polished, suave, and courageous, but above all he was ambitious and a schemer—yet such a jolly, likable schemer! "The Adonis of the court" was lithe and lean, with dark hair, a full beard, and lively brown eyes. He excelled in sports, was a graceful dancer, a witty conversationalist, and spent money lavishly, especially in the matter of his own apparel. Women found him fascinating.

Though Jane admired him and laughed at his jokes, she

did not wholly trust him, perhaps because she knew that if either Mary or Bess had accepted him, he would not now be married to her beloved Catherine. His marriage to the Queen Dowager had brought him added prestige, an increased fortune, and would undoubtedly strengthen his hold over the King. Apparently Catherine had no suspicion that in marrying her he was not motivated wholly by love, and certainly he seemed to adore her. Did Catherine know that before proposing to her he had offered himself to Bess? Jane was sure she was ignorant of this; anyhow, what did it matter now?

Thus began the happiest period of Jane's life. No more would she be slapped and criticized. No more would she be lonely and unloved. Her surroundings were luxurious. Like Bess, she had been given her own spacious apartment with her own attendants.

Thomas, Catherine, Bess, and Jane formed a rollicking, carefree family. If the weather was fair, when the girls had finished their lessons, they joined the lovers in the garden. Sometimes there would be riddles, but usually they played noisy and strenuous games: tennis, quoits, and frequently Hoodman Blind.

After a few weeks Jane noticed that whenever Thomas was hoodman, Bess managed to be caught. Since she was excessively ticklish, he often would tickle her, but more often she paid the forfeit with a kiss, blushing furiously. Catherine seemed to suspect nothing, and of course there was no harm in the game, but finally Jane, who could not bear the thought of Catherine's being hurt, forced herself to speak to Bess one day when they found themselves alone.

"Bess," she pleaded earnestly, "I beg you to stop."

"Stop what?" Elizabeth's eyes brightened warningly. "I do not know what you mean."

"You're flirting with Lord Thomas. Don't deny it!"

"Why, Jane Grey! Yes, I do deny it."

Jane Seymour, mother of Edward VI:
Hans Holbein. Windsor Castle

ABOVE: Edward VI: Hans Holbein
The Metropolitan Museum of Art, New York,
The Jules S. Bache Collection, 1949

LEFT: Edward VI:
Unknown artist. Windsor Castle

John Dudley, Duke of Northumberland: Unknown artist

"Bess, please. Lady Catherine loves him so."

"I could have had him if I had wanted him," answered Bess flippantly, toying with her many necklaces.

She had beautiful hands, and this was one way she had of calling attention to them. She was fourteen and an attractive girl. Her body was small, slim, with a tiny waist, a fact that she carefully emphasized by wearing extremely full skirts. Her brows were light and thin, barely discernible. Her red hair was always frizzed. She spent enormous amounts on clothes and had an extensive wardrobe. In spite of her adornment she could never be called beautiful, though she always considered herself so.

"We will not talk about something that is none of your business," she announced now with an edge of temper. "What's the harm in a little flirtation? I've never had much fun in my life, you know."

"But we both love Lady Catherine and she has been very good to you."

"I should think you would have learned by this time," Bess answered tartly, "to mind your own affairs. I forbid you to mention this again."

"But—"

"And if you go prattling to the Queen—"

"No, never. I love the Queen too much to hurt her. I cannot understand adults. Anyone can see that you attract Thomas, and yet he's undoubtedly in love with his wife!"

"He only took her because I refused him," retorted Bess.

"Why did you, if you're fond of him?"

Bess shrugged. "One has to think of the future. I am second in line to the throne. Edward is not robust. Mary is sickly. Someday . . . someday I shall rule England! Meanwhile, I mean to enjoy myself as much as I can. Am I to blame because Catherine is blind?"

But Catherine was not as blind as she seemed to be.

The Greatest Grief

Because of Somerset's unrelenting machinations, Thomas, Catherine, Bess, and Jane were balked in their attempts to see as much of the King as they wished, but when Uncle Thomas and his wife could manage to secure an interview, they usually took Jane with them and contrived to leave the young people alone for a short time. On such occasions the elders would return to Chelsea Manor, leaving Jane to follow them later, and would smile softly at the happiness of the two young people at the mere sight of each other. Edward's and Jane's joy whenever they met indicated that, when they were the proper age, they would glady accede to the projected marriage plans.

Edward, since he had become king, had changed into a nervous, tense, and troubled boy, always resentful of the Protector's stern control. He suffered acutely because the English people—*his* people—were miserable under Somerset's misrule. Jane noticed, one day while visiting Edward at Hampton Court, that his sight was deteriorating, and Catherine had already mentioned that he suffered a great deal from headaches. Thomas had added that these were caused by the strain the boy was under. On this particular day, though Edward had no headache, he was obviously keyed up and disturbed.

"Oh, Jane, if you knew how pleasant it is to have even these few minutes alone with you! And it will be only a few moments! I'm never allowed more than a quarter of an hour alone. I'm watched all the time."

"Do you think it would be different if the Queen Dowager and the lord admiral were your protectors?"

He sighed deeply and shrugged. "Perhaps. Half the time I do not know whether to believe Uncle Thomas or Uncle Edward. One of them tells me one thing, the other tells me the opposite."

"I know how you're being torn between them. Oh, Edward, if only I could do something do save you from being upset like this!"

"Neither of us can do anything," he replied dolefully. "It takes a dreadfully long time before one gets to be eighteen."

"Lord Thomas and Lady Catherine really love you."

"I know Catherine does, but Uncle Thomas? Behind that mask of gaiety and generosity, he's self-seeking." He spoke bitterly. "The only people who love me for myself are you and Catherine."

"I do love you, Edward. Sometimes I wish you weren't king. Then we could see each other as often as we liked. Tell me, has either Lady Catherine or Lord Thomas ever mentioned that they hope you and I will marry? They've never said so to me, not a word. And I have never mentioned it to them. I can't, somehow."

"Oh, they haven't said it—openly. So far there have only been subtle hints." He moved about the room wretchedly. "I've thought about it, too."

"You have?"

"You're so sweet, so understanding, and I love you more than anything or anyone in the world! We have the same religion, the same interests, and yet . . . I must consider the country. You do understand that, don't you?"

"Of course. Of course. And you know, Edward, that I love you—as a brother, as my dearest friend."

As usual they had only these few minutes alone, for now they were interrupted by the entrance of the Duke and

Duchess of Somerset, both plainly disturbed about something.

"It is not well, Your Majesty," said the duke sternly, "that you have private audiences without my consent. I assure you that I am thinking only of Your Majesty's good."

"I warrant Lord Thomas and his wife are to blame for it," cried the duchess, who was obviously on the verge of indulging one of her violent tantrums. "Oh, that woman! I beg Your Majesty to intercede for me in the matter of precedence!"

If Edward had any fear of the Somersets, he carefully refrained from showing it. "I ask Your Grace to remember that you are referring to my dearest mother," he replied coldly.

"Nevertheless, I am the wife of the Protector. As such I should be ahead of any woman in the realm, yet she takes precedence over me! Must I give place to her who in her former state was only Latimer's widow and who is now fain to cast herself for protection on my husband's younger brother? If Master Admiral doesn't teach his wife better manners, I will!"

Edward sighed. Jane realized that he must be constantly subjected to such pettiness.

"What is the complaint this time?" he asked wearily. "If it were in your power, you would keep the Queen Dowager from court entirely. Let me remind you that she has taken the place of the mother I have never known. If I could have my way I would see her more often. But what has she done now that causes Your Ladyship this irritation?"

"I maintain, Your Majesty, that I should take precedence over her, instead of the reverse. I am the wife of the greatest peer in the land."

"As Queen Dowager, Catherine does have precedence over you, Madame," Edward replied. "That is a point of etiquette that cannot be changed."

Rebuffed, Anne Seymour stared at him arrogantly. Jane knew that she did not intend to abandon this matter of precedence so easily, but for the present she said no more about it. Somerset, usually a sour, humorless man, smiled at Jane. He appeared weary and looked much older than his age. His long, thin hands reminded her of talons, and his smile had no warmth behind it.

"It is time, Lady Jane, that your parents—pardon, your guardian—arrange a marriage for you. You are eleven now, are you not? And not yet plighted. And speaking of marriage, Your Majesty, too, ere long must consider the matter. Sire, it would please your court were you to marry my daughter Anne. As the King's Grace knows, she has received the finest education. She is also of your religion. As for the Lady Jane Grey, the duchess and I would be pleased to form an alliance between her and our son, the Earl of Hertford."

"Jane and I are too young to consider marriage," said Edward. "Your Grace, I think, is overhasty."

"Her Ladyship knows my son well. He has oft been a guest at Bradgate."

Edward sighed. "Pray, sir, let us hear no more of this."

"As you wish, sire."

The King looked, Jane thought, very tired, and she asked his permission to leave. On the way back to Chelsea Manor she was troubled. She knew that someday she must marry and she also knew that it was a matter in which her own desires would not be considered. The choice of her future husband must be determined by her parents, or, now that she was the ward of Lord Thomas, by him and Catherine.

She considered being married to Seymour's son someday, and the prospect was not displeasing. She liked the youth, who was as different from his parents as she was from hers. If she could not marry Edward—and she did not believe that such a union could ever be brought about—then she might eventually find contentment with the Earl of Hertford.

Arriving at Chelsea Manor, she went directly to her apartment but she did not open her books. It was a bleak day in January, and the chilliness did nothing to alleviate her depression. She was sorely troubled about Edward. He had looked so thin, so pale, so taut. Always, always conflict surrounding him! Oh, for the day when he could be free of Somerset's irksome yoke!

He would be a fine, wise king. As he grew older he would increase in strength, and one day, rid of dominance, he would find a way to right the many wrongs that had been perpetrated by Somerset, for Edward loved his people. He would bring them prosperity and contentment. Like herself, they were waiting for that day.

She thought of his being married to some beautiful foreign princess, and the prospect brought no joy. On the other hand, if Thomas and Catherine could bring about a betrothal between Edward and herself . . . but while Somerset was in power that would be impossible.

A week later Catherine made a discovery. Everything, even the possible marriage between Edward and Jane, was dwarfed by the fact that at last she was to have a child of her own. She, who had mothered the children of three former husbands, was to be a mother! She was happier now than ever before.

Jane and Bess were delighted when she told them. Thomas, too, rejoiced. He was sure it would be a son.

A few days after this, Catherine gravely entered Jane's room and quietly asked Mrs. Ashley to leave her alone with the girl.

"Is something the matter, Madame?" asked Jane.

"I only came to tell you that our Eliza is leaving."

"Oh?"

"I think it wise that I send her away."

"Yes, Madame."

"You do not ask why."

"It is a wise decision, Madame. I understand."

"You have noticed it, too, then! We shall not ever refer to it again. She is only a child, really. It is natural, I suppose, that at fifteen a girl should think it rather exciting to flirt with an older man, though such behavior is foolish. She and I will part amicably. We will still be friends. I hope we shall always be friends."

Jane, knowing Catherine so well, realized that she was deeply hurt. Since it was winter they no longer met in the garden, and the boisterous games that had been transferred to the great hall came to an abrupt end. But there were no altercations. Thomas remained gay and gallant. Catherine was poised and gracious. Bess was decorous, amiable, and seemingly bore no grudge against her stepmother.

Before leaving for Hatfield Castle a few days later, she entered Jane's room to say good-by.

"I hope you'll visit me, Jane," she said calmly. "You know, of course, why I'm being sent away. It is because the lord admiral loves me too well and the Queen is jealous. Oh, she was extremely nice about it, and I really have no hard feelings toward her."

The two girls embraced and Jane watched from her window as Bess, traveling in royal style, rode away from Chelsea Manor.

Soon after this Catherine declared that she was weary of London and the constant intrigues of court life and wanted to get away from the city to some quiet place, there to await the birth of her child. Thomas, humoring her, suggested that they go to Hanworth.

But a strange restlessness possessed Catherine now. When they had been at Hanworth for several weeks, she suggested that they move to Oatlands, but this castle, too, failed to please her.

Thomas thought she might like Sudeley Castle, a noble building in Gloucester. So they packed up again and a month later, with Catherine riding in a wagon with many pillows, they made the six-day journey.

Sudeley was just what Catherine wanted. It was a vast Gothic structure, richly furnished and beautifully quiet, with an enormous park. Catherine's chamber was hung with tapestry and her large tester bed had curtains of red taffeta. The furniture was upholstered in Genoa velvet. There were brocades from Venice, silk drapes from China, cabinets of ebony inlaid with mother-of-pearl.

Jane's bedroom, near Catherine's, was hung with blue silk, its floor covered by a Turkish carpet. She, too, loved Sudeley. Here one could forget about London, about Somerset, about Elizabeth. Or so Jane thought, for Catherine seemed serenely untroubled. But the memory of Elizabeth, as it turned out later, was preying heavily on her mind.

Catherine's retinue was as large as it had always been, with ladies in waiting, maids of honor, gentlemen in ordinary, and yeomen of the guard. Everyone seemed to feel happily at home, and the whole court waited expectantly for the birth of the Queen Dowager's baby.

No sooner had they arrived than it became the delight of Catherine and Jane to fit up the nursery. No prince of the realm ever had one more luxurious. Time passed in joyous preparation. Twice a day, led by one of Catherine's chaplains, there was divine worship, but at other times Catherine and Jane were sure to be found in the nursery. One would think, Jane said, that Catherine was about to give birth to an heir to the throne.

The day nursery, or outer room, was hung with costly tapestry. Every cushion was of cloth of gold. The taborets had embroidered covers. The inner chamber, also hung with tapestry, contained a lavish cradle, a bed for the nurse, and furnishings upholstered in crimson taffeta, with sumptuous draperies at the four windows. The child must even have its own plate service.

At last everything was ready.

"Jane," said Catherine, her smile radiant, "I want you to be my baby's godmother. Now, you mustn't worry about me. I feel fine. I have always been blessed with excellent health. I have naught to fear."

"What a fortunate child this is," said Jane, "to have a mother who will love it so much and care for it so tenderly."

Kate touched Jane's hand fondly. "Its coming will not make me love you any the less, sweet."

A few days later, on August 30, 1548, Catherine gave birth to a daughter.

Though he had expected a son, her husband was filled with rejoicing. When Jane was permitted to enter the sickroom several hours after the birth, Catherine was sleeping. The girl took a chair near the bed, gazing upon the face of this woman whom she loved so greatly. Then she noticed how pale Catherine was. Presently, without opening her eyes, Catherine began moving restlessly and moaning softly, as though she were having some terrible dream.

"Catherine, Your Grace," whispered Jane anxiously. "Wake up! It's over now and everything is all right. Your baby is healthy and beautiful."

Catherine opened her eyes and reached for Jane's hand. "Stay with me," she murmured, her eyes filled with fear. "Stay with me, Jane."

"Yes. Do you feel badly, My Lady? Shall I call His Lordship? Your ladies? The doctor?"

"No Stay with me. I . . . I know . . ."

Whatever Catherine intended to say, she thought better of it. A few seconds later she began tossing again. Presently the room was filled with people who did not seem concerned about this, but told each other what a fine baby it was and how happy they were. Thomas, lover-like, kissed his wife and sat holding her hand. Now and then her eyes stared at him, strangely questioning, oddly accusing.

The next day she was feverish. On the third day she was decidedly worse. The doctor, his countenance grave, pronounced her illness to be puerperal fever. Jane scarcely left Catherine, who tossed continually and was often irritable. When Jane was absent from the sickroom even for a few minutes Catherine would ask reproachfully, "Where have you been?" And once she whispered, "Jane, I have been poisoned!"

"No, Madame, don't think that! Who would do such a thing?"

"I'm sure I have been poisoned!"

"Oh, no, My Lady! There is no one in the world who would want to see you dead! The doctor says it is a kind of fever. You will get well! You must!"

Catherine began tossing again.

"Jane," she muttered, when they were alone on another occasion, "I shall not live long."

"Don't say that, My Lady!" cried Jane in anguish. "No! You're not going to die!"

"He has poisoned me, Jane. He wants to be rid of me. He loves Eliza!"

"No! He loves you, only you!"

But Catherine did not seem to hear her. Her husband came in and, sitting by her bed, took her hand, holding it tenderly, speaking in a gentle voice, trying to soothe her.

"You don't care about me!" she cried.

"Why, sweetheart, don't say such things."

"I think you would like to see me dead."

He smoothed back the hair from her forehead and insisted that he loved her.

Some days later, when she became coherent again, she made her will, leaving everything to him. As her illness continued, Jane moved in and out of the sickroom as though through a nightmare. Thomas was the soul of devotion. Hour after hour he sat stroking his wife's hand. Catherine's ladies tiptoed in and out, speaking in whispers. Sometimes Catherine spoke sensibly. At other times, in her delirium, she imagined that her husband was laughing at her suffering, that he was eager to be rid of her and marry Bess. Why, Jane wondered, should she be obsessed by this thought? Could there be any truth in it?

"Catherine must not die!" she kept saying. And she prayed wildly, "Dear Lord, don't let Catherine die!"

But eight days after the birth of her child, between two and three in the morning, when Jane was alone with her, Catherine Parr died.

"My Lady, My Lady," Jane pleaded piteously, "don't leave me! You're all I have. I need you!"

Presently she knew that Catherine no longer heard.

The funeral took place at Sudeley. Jane, as a member of the blood royal, was chief mourner. In deep black, with six women of Catherine's retinue, she sat in the chapel with the casket throughout the night, while the candles made a wan, flickering glow upon that serene, beloved face. It could not be that Catherine was dead. The walls and rails, covered by black cloth, were only part of a horrible dream.

At the funeral it all became real, frightfully real. Jane walked directly behind the lead coffin, which was carried on the shoulders of six of Catherine's gentlemen. Then it was over, and Jane knew that the happiest days of her life were over, too. Numb with grief, she did not protest when her parents sent for her to return to Bradgate. Thomas seems to have agreed readily to her leaving.

All the way to Bradgate she was dazed, not caring how fast or how slowly they went, unmindful of the heat or the rain. When she finally greeted her parents she was too grief-stricken to answer their cross-questioning. Her grief only irritated them.

"Answer me true!" commanded Lady Frances, her gray eyes hostile. "One of Catherine's gentlemen who escorted you told me that she accused the lord admiral of poisoning her!"

"She was delirious when she said that."

"If she thought he had poisoned her, why did she leave her entire fortune to him?"

"Because she loved him."

"Had she any reason to suspect that he was in love with Bess?"

"No. No."

"Why was Bess sent away, then?"

The questioning continued daily while Jane's grief, instead of diminishing, intensified as she realized more and more fully how great was her loss.

A week after her arrival at Bradgate, Henry Grey received a letter from Thomas Seymour. His wife's death had been such a shock, he wrote, that he had not known what he was doing when he allowed Jane to return to them. But now he wanted Jane with him. She would live with him and his mother at Seymour House. His tiny daughter had been entrusted to the care of the Duchess of Somerset.

But now the Greys were not certain that they would turn their daughter over to him again. They hedged. Despite her present pallor, Jane had grown more beautiful during the past year. Was there still a possibility that even without Catherine's help, the lord admiral could bring about a marriage between her and the King?

On September 23, the Greys, with their numerous household, set off for London. Scarcely had they arrived when Thomas, accompanied by Sharington, paid them a visit.

Though he had shown much sorrow at his wife's death, which had occurred only a few weeks earlier, he now seemed completely recovered. Still in mourning, he was nevertheless dapper and confident.

Vast though their wealth was, the Greys were now living

beyond their means, and somehow he had found that out. He lost no time in coming to the point.

"I want Jane back."

"Why, My Lord?" asked Lady Frances shrewdly.

"My dear wife was fond of her. I, too, am fond of her. Give her back to me. She will be in the care of my mother. Come, why should you hesitate?"

"Well, My Lord," said Grey, twirling his waxed mustache slowly, "I am about to make an alliance for her with the young Earl of Hertford. To turn the girl over to you would anger the Lord Protector."

"Do not be so hasty, my friend," answered Thomas in his cocksure way. "If I can set the King at liberty, I warrant His Majesty shall marry none other than Jane!"

"If you can set the King at liberty?" asked Lady Frances. "How does Your Lordship propose to accomplish this?"

"My plans, Your Ladyship, are my own. I have no time to plead or argue. I want the guardianship of Lady Jane. I know you are in debt, therefore I offer you two thousand pounds for her—five hundred down this minute!"

"Two thousand pounds!" Henry Grey exchanged a glance with his wife.

"When," asked Lady Frances with a smile, "would you like Her Ladyship to be sent to you?"

Northumberland

When her parents told Jane that she was to return to Seymour House she asked no questions. It was always a relief to be away from home.

At Seymour House she and her attendants were left entirely alone. The old Dowager Lady Seymour seemed more careworn and worried than ever, living her solitary life aloof from worldly glitter, yet no stranger to its turmoil, for though her sons never confided in her, she knew that Thomas had lately embarked upon a daring and dangerous game. Had Catherine lived, she might have served as a deterrent to his scheming or at least would have seen to it that he acted cautiously, but now his ambition soared. Telling himself that he had waited long enough, he plunged ahead recklessly. His impatience—burning, driving impatience—to depose his brother and become regent obscured his judgment. He had control of Jane. Now he must get control of the King and the kingdom.

Jane rarely saw him. When they chanced to meet in the hall he seemed to be always rushing off somewhere, tense, abstracted. She was not curious. No longer did things matter to her. Her best friend, her true mother, was dead. Now there was only Edward.

She knew that he must be grieving, too, and several times she wrote for permission to see him, but the Protector was still determined to keep them apart. Somerset's anxieties were increased now, as his spies reported the activities of his brother. He knew everything that Thomas was doing. Let the fool continue!

After regaining guardianship of Jane, Thomas again tried to secure his position by a marriage with Princess Elizabeth. The girl had certainly encouraged him at Chelsea Manor and he was sure that she would now fall eagerly into his arms. But to his surprise, Bess was evasive. Though Thomas Seymour was undoubtedly Elizabeth's first love, she was wise beyond her years. Still, he did not give up hope of eventually winning her.

Meanwhile, he went further. He spent his own vast wealth, plus the fortune left him by Catherine, to muster a small army secretly. When these money reserves were exhausted he contacted various pirates, beguiling them into contributing to his cause by assuring them of protection later. He bribed certain important men, hoping to bring them to his side. When he returned to Seymour House on the night of January 1, 1549, he was filled with confidence.

"Rest well this night, My Lady," he said as he entered Jane's room, his eyes glowing, his voice ringing with good cheer. "Aye, rest well, for by tomorrow night I shall have freed the King, and soon your betrothal to him will take place."

"But, Your Lordship, I . . ."

"Everything is arranged," he announced with a blithe wave of his slender, ringed hand.

"What is arranged, My Lord?"

"I shall marry our Eliza and you shall marry the King. England will rejoice in a new regent. Oh, I have waited so long for this moment! Now, pleasant dreams—and wish me well!"

He walked out, striding cockily.

Jane retired soon after he had swaggered out of her room, but she was unable to sleep. How could he think of marrying

Bess when it was not yet three months since Catherine's death? Had Catherine been right when she accused him of poisoning her in order to wed the younger girl? And how could he possibly take over the regency?

Mrs. Ellen awakened her early next morning, plainly agitated.

"My Lady, My Lady! Wake up!"

"What is it?"

"His Lordship has just been arrested and taken to the Tower!"

Jane leaped out of bed and rushed to Lady Seymour. The old lady was sobbing piteously.

"He is as good as dead," she moaned.

"What has he done?"

"There is no hope. They have clear evidence of treason!"

"But surely the duke would not have his own brother beheaded!"

"If you think that, you do not know my elder son."

In the next few days Jane learned all that Thomas had done. What distressed her most was to see how his erstwhile friends abandoned him at his trial. The Greys were among the first to give evidence against him.

After questioning Catherine's ladies, Somerset started the rumor that Thomas had poisoned his wife in order to marry Princess Elizabeth. Elizabeth's servants were also arrested, questioned, and then released. They told of the flirtation between Thomas and the Princess that had gone on at Chelsea Manor, and how he had wanted to marry her a few weeks after Catherine's death. Jane was not interrogated.

Barely a week after the arrest, she was surprised to receive a note from the King asking her to come to Hampton Court. It was written hastily on wrapping paper, for Seymour allowed the boy no proper stationery. Edward had managed somehow to smuggle the message out.

Jane, a small, black-clad figure, hastened through the huge

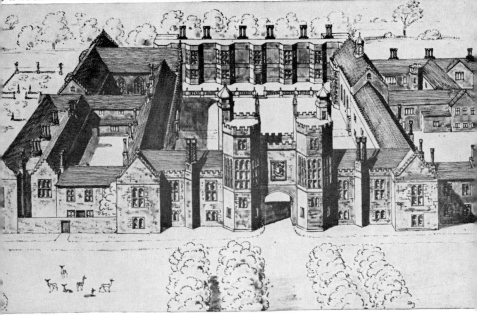

Newhall Castle (later called Beaulieu),
one of Princess Mary's residences

From *Palaces and Progresses of Elizabeth,* by Ian Dunlop

Princess Elizabeth: Unknown artist. Windsor Castle

Guilford Dudley, husband of Lady Jane Grey: Unknown artist

Gothic banqueting hall to the private apartments of the King, where she found Edward, white, thin, harried, alone.

"Close the door, Jane," he said grouchily, with no joy at the sight of her.

She forgot to kneel, so shocked was she by the greeting. "Edward! Are you ill?"

"No, no, I'm well enough. Sit down, Jane. I want you to tell me the truth. I know you will. You know what Uncle Thomas is accused of. Somerset insists that I sign his death warrant. I might forgive him everything—yes, everything— except . . . except the accusation that he poisoned my sweet mother in order to marry Bess."

"No, Edward, I'm sure Lady Catherine wasn't poisoned."

"You can't know for sure, can you?"

"No, but—"

"That he would try to marry Bess so soon after Catherine's death!" Edward shuddered. "Did he and Bess want to dethrone me?"

"No, Edward, not that, and you mustn't think so. Lord Thomas wanted to become your guardian and the ruler of the realm, and he thought to strengthen his position by a marriage with Bess. He was always kind to his wife, especially after she fell ill. He was gentle with her, patient and attentive. She was delirious. She said things she didn't mean."

"But there must have been some basis for her words. Tell me, Jane! I must know the truth!"

"Well, at Chelsea Manor he and Bess did give the Queen cause for suspicion—that was why Bess was sent away. But it was only a flirtation, nothing more, and mostly it was Bess's fault. She acted boldly. She encouraged him."

"Flirtation! And Catherine not cold in her grave before he tries to marry Bess! Oh, it looks bad, Jane. I could forgive him anything but this—that he poisoned my dearest mother."

"No, Edward, I'm sure that was only a rumor started by his enemies."

"From all the evidence, it would seem that there is truth in it. I was fond of him! He was good to me and generous, but . . ." He moaned, "Oh, what a world we live in! What an ugly, conniving world! Where is honor, where is decency? I . . . I don't want to talk any more, Jane. Please . . . please go."

"Yes, Edward. I know that this, coming so soon after Lady Catherine's death, is almost more than you can bear. If only I could say something to comfort you!"

"I will do as Uncle Edward insists. I will sign that death warrant. I . . . Please go, Jane."

"Yes, Edward."

She knew that he did not want her to see him cry and she left the room swiftly, not looking back.

Thomas Seymour was beheaded on Tower Hill on March 20, 1549, a little over six months after Catherine's death.

Jane was back at Bradgate now, for as soon as the Greys had given evidence against Thomas they had scampered out of town and at once sent a hundred men-at-arms to bring Jane from Seymour House.

The death of Lord Thomas brought them to the realization that there was now no possibility of their daughter's marrying Edward, and they lost no time in betrothing her to Somerset's son, the young and personable Earl of Hertford. Perhaps because of their nervousness and fear, their cruelty toward Jane increased.

Partly to avoid them, partly to forget her sense of loss, Jane was almost incessantly at her studies these days. The only person who lightened her gloom was another tutor, a good-looking young man of about thirty, John Aylmer. With him Jane could forget her pain, for he was not only a great teacher but a gentle, high-minded soul.

In the autumn of 1549, Roger Ascham returned to Bradgate and resumed his duties as an additional tutor. He found the whole family, with the exception of Jane, gaily playing games in the garden. He went at once to his pupil.

"On such a lovely day it seems a shame to be indoors. At twelve one should have amusement as well as books. Why is my illustrious Lady not out in the garden joining in the games?" he asked with concern.

Jane looked at him and smiled a welcome, but she said nothing.

"How do you get along with Aylmer?" Ascham asked.

Jane broke down now. "Oh, sir," she answered, her voice trembling, "one of the greatest benefits that God ever gave me is that He sent me so gentle a schoolmaster as Mr. Aylmer! My parents are sharp and severe. When I am in the presence of either my father or mother, whether I speak, keep silence, sit, stand or go, eat, drink, be merry or sad, be sewing, playing, dancing, or doing anything else, I must do it, as it were, in such weight, measure, and number, even as perfectly as God made the world, or else I am so sharply taunted, so cruelly threatened, yes, presented sometimes with pinches, nips, slaps, and other ways—which I will not name for the honor I bear them—that I think myself in hell till the time comes when I must go to Mr. Aylmer, who teaches me so gently, with such fair allurements to learning, that I think all the time of nothing whilst I am with him. And when I am called from him I fall on weeping, because whatever I do else but learning is full of great trouble and fear!"

Strange words, coming from a girl of twelve, Ascham thought; but she had described her position accurately and he knew it. It was well, he mused, that she could find solace in books. Poor little Lady Jane! To her, learning was an escape, and she sorely needed an escape. Not only could she speak and read Hebrew and Arabian now, but she was equally fluent in French, Greek, Latin, and Italian.

She remained at Bradgate for over a year, making a few visits to Mary, who was then at Beaulieu (Henry VIII had changed its name from Newhall); but though she was away from London she was not unaware of the terrible things that were taking place there.

The nobles as well as the commoners had never liked Somerset, and after he had connived in his brother Thomas' death, the men who formed the Council of Regency began quietly to bring about his downfall. Put Thomas in prison —yes, and keep him there; but fratricide—ah, that was another thing!

Chief among those who operated clandestinely to bring about Somerset's loss of influence was the arrogant Earl of Warwick. John Dudley, Earl of Warwick, now in his late forties, was a handsome man, tall, with a long beard and full mustache, who had gained some reputation as an expert swordsman. His longing to supersede Somerset had become a living force within him. Skillfully, with a cunning even beyond that of Somerset, he undermined the regent's support in the council.

Once when Jane was visiting Mary the subject was broached. Mary seemed totally unmoved by what was happening. "Somerset is losing power," she remarked coolly at breakfast one morning. "I hear the Earl of Warwick is rising. But he, too, is an evil man, even worse than Edward Seymour. What is the opinion of your father?"

"My father never discusses such things with me. In fact, I try to avoid him as much as I can."

"And I understand why. But he will surely support the one who is rising and abandon the one who is falling. I remember he was quick to support Anne Boleyn's cause against that of my sainted mother. So he is sure to be on Warwick's side. As for Somerset and Lord Thomas, they grew rich because my father gave them much of the wealth of the desecrated monasteries. The people loathe Somerset. There have been uprisings in Norfolk, you know. The treasury is empty. The soldiers are unpaid. Is it true that you are betrothed to young Seymour?"

"Yes."

"And you are satisfied?"

"Yes. I think he is very nice. I haven't seen him many times, but I like him well enough. I am sure I shall grow to love him."

"But never as much as you love Edward?"

Jane blushed.

"Oh, come, Jane! I know how much you care for Edward." Mary changed the subject, having more important things to consider. "The Somerset faction and the Warwick faction are strong parties. Warwick, I hear, is supported by Wriothesley. I hear Warwick has his spies even in the King's palace. We both know that Somerset has held Edward in virtual captivity. No one, not even I, can visit Edward except through Somerset, who claims that Edward's health is too poor. Well, as for me, I shall remain aloof from both factions."

"Mary, is it true that Edward grows more sickly?"

"I hear so, but it is almost a year since I've seen him. Well, any day now we can expect Somerset's fall. Then we shall go from bad to worse. I detest Warwick!"

Mary's prediction came true shortly thereafter. The council withdrew its support from Somerset, forcing him to retire. The office of protector, though not the title, now went to Warwick, who soon contrived to have Edward create him the Duke of Northumberland.

Jane was summoned one afternoon into her parents' presence.

"We wish to inform Your Ladyship," announced Lady Frances, "that we have broken your betrothal to the Earl of Hertford."

At once Jane understood why. They had no desire to be

affiliated with a family that was no longer in power. They were determined to break all ties with Somerset, who had been put in prison and then released after being heavily fined. Now they were on the side of Northumberland. Their announcement of the broken engagement brought Jane a pang of sadness, for she had liked her fiancé.

"I regret that you find it advisable to do this," she said. "Though his father is no longer regent, I would gladly marry the earl."

"It is not for you to decide this matter," Lady Frances reminded her sharply.

"No, Madame. I know that my wishes are not to be considered. Please, may I . . . may I ask if you have seen the King?"

"I saw His Majesty recently," replied Henry Grey solemnly. "He did not look well. What a pity the King does not resemble his father!"

"Shall I be permitted to see him when we return to the city?"

"It is doubtful," said Lady Frances.

"May I be excused now?"

They nodded.

Jane wondered as she left them whom they would betroth her to now. She had the feeling that they would not delay in this matter. Her sister Catherine had been affianced to Henry Herbert, son of the Earl of Pembroke. It was a wealthy family, and though Catherine disliked her fiancé she was nevertheless proud that her parents had arranged such a match for her. They were now negotiating for the troth of little Mary, though she was six years younger than Jane, and a misshapen dwarf.

Catherine was waiting for her when she returned to her apartment. "So, you're no longer betrothed!" Catherine began. "How sad. You're older than I and not yet bespoken. Oh, I envied you when you were betrothed to the Protector's son! Now we must pretend to despise Somerset and to admire Northumberland. I wonder if the King is happy about the change?"

"Oh, I wish I could see Edward!" cried Jane. "I wish we weren't growing up. I wish he and I could be children again and play together as we used to."

Northumberland was now all-powerful, and he was even more of a schemer than the Seymours had been. Edward's increasing weakness and frequent illnesses brought the realization that the boy would probably never live to rule England, and the wily regent now began plotting to keep Mary from the throne. He had had a taste of power now and it had intoxicated him. He reasoned that if Mary were on the throne he would automatically be relegated to a lesser role, so he began to circulate the story that she was "a poor miserable invalid, fit for nothing but to be shut up in her palace." If possible, he intended to keep her there.

In 1551 a great change took place in the Grey's fortunes. Lady Frances' two half brothers died. The dukedom of Suffolk, which had originally been given to Charles Brandon, thus became vacant and was given to Henry Grey. The new Duke and Duchess of Suffolk were now the inheritors of vast wealth as well as lands and castles.

The next meeting between Jane and Edward took place in November, 1551, when they were both fourteen, on the occasion of an entertainment given for the Scottish Queen Regent, Mary of Guise, at Westminster. Edward did not dance, but Jane danced with Guilford Dudley, Northumberland's favorite son, whom she met now for the first time. He was tall, well built, good looking, yet before the evening ended Jane knew that she abhorred him, and he made no pretense of finding her attractive.

Bess was there, too, having made a grand show as she rode

through London accompanied by about two hundred lords, ladies, knights, and gentlemen. She flirted with Robert Dudley, another son of Northumberland, whom everyone called "Robin," easily the most fascinating man at court. His bride, Amy, pretended not to notice. Bess seemed to have forgotten Lord Thomas completely.

Edward treated her coldly, for Northumberland and his henchmen had succeeded in estranging the two. Since it was such a formal occasion, Jane had no opportunity to speak to Edward alone. A genuflection before the throne was all that was permitted her.

As soon as the state visit of the royal guest from Scotland ended, the Greys left for Bradgate, traveling with their customary impressive escort of one hundred and fifty horsemen, plus maids, grooms, and other servants.

In April, 1552, Edward contracted a severe case of measles, and from this point his health deteriorated month by month. It was soon obvious to the hangers-on at the court that the boy might not live to become king.

Henry Grey, though outwardly Northumberland's friend, was one of those who believed in preparing for any course the future might take. He now attempted to become more friendly with the sickly Princess Mary, since she was next in line for the throne. One day he summoned Jane and told her to write an affectionate letter to Mary.

"If Edward should die," he said callously, "we must not forget that Mary will be queen. That is one thing Northumberland will be unable to change."

Jane's small face paled. "Edward won't die!" she cried.

Her father continued as though she had not spoken. "Of course, if Northumberland can prevent it, she'll never be queen, and who knows? After all, he may find some way to do so. None of us would like to see Catholicism re-established. We have often discussed this in the council. But it is safe to be on the—"

Jane was not listening. The thought that Edward might die brought terror. "Edward mustn't die!" she murmured.

"Mary has always been friendly with you," her father continued glibly. "Tell her in your letter how often she has been in your thoughts, how you long to see her, how you have heard that she has a cold. Bring the letter to me for my approval before you send it."

"Yes, Your Grace. But please, please could you arrange for me to see His Majesty? If only for a few minutes?"

"I will talk to the duke about it."

A few days later he sent his daughter word that an interview had been aranged on the condition that she stay no more than a quarter of an hour.

Jane and Edward had not met for over a year, and the change in him made her want to cry. He had failed to recover strength and lay on a couch, weak, white, and listless.

"Jane, Jane," he said unsteadily, "it's been so long since I've seen you."

"Edward! Oh, Edward, I've been so worried about you!"

"I've been very ill."

"I know. If only I could stay with you and take care of you! But soon you'll be strong again—stronger than ever. Is Northumberland kind to you?"

"A little better than Somerset. Not quite so stern. But I don't trust him."

"You must get strong, Edward. It's only a few years now until you become the real ruler of England. You will make a wonderful king. The people love you. They say, 'When Edward's on the throne all our wrongs will be righted.'"

His dull eyes lit up and he raised himself to a sitting position. "Do they really say that?"

"Yes, truly. They put all their hope in you."

"I *must* get well. I must not fail them. Mary must never rule England. Catholicism must not be restored!"

"I had hoped you had outgrown that prejudice."

"No. At all costs the reform movement must continue!"

"Let's not discuss that. It seems to excite you. Would you like me to read to you?"

"I'd rather talk. It's so restful just being with you. Why don't you come more often?"

"I've asked to, but it wasn't permitted. I would have liked to come and nurse you during your illness, but I could only pray for you. Lady Catherine is gone. You are my only friend. If anything should happen to you, Edward, I wouldn't want to live. I love you so much. It's a different love than I used to feel as a child. I think of you all the time. Even if I cannot come often, you mustn't think that I don't care. I'm fifteen now. We're both fifteen. Our play days are over, but—"

There was a knock on the door. He sighed restively. "I'm never left alone! I wish they'd leave me alone! I—" His voice rose. "Well, come in."

Northumberland entered, sank to one knee, then rose, approaching the King with a smile. "And how are you to-day, sire? Better, I hope? The kingdom rejoices in Your Majesty's recovery. Apparently the Lady Jane has been good medicine."

"It is always good to see her," replied Edward coldly. "I regret that her visits must be so rare."

Northumberland maintained his smile. "I know you are fond of Her Ladyship, my liege."

"Jane has always been close to me, sir, even though months pass without seeing her."

The older man gave Jane a candid inspection. She was small-boned, delicate, with a beguiling young dignity and poise. Her long-lashed eyes were innocent, her soft mouth lovely.

Though Northumberland was determined that neither Mary nor Elizabeth should see Edward, it pleased him that the King was still devoted to Jane Grey. Yes, the girl was beautiful, sitting there relaxed, in her simple long-sleeved gown of black velvet with a deep square-cut neckline and a narrow beaded belt. Her throat was unadorned by the many necklaces that had become so fashionable, and she wore little jewelry. Jane was part of Northumberland's plan, which as yet he had not divulged to anyone.

Once he had been servile to Somerset and made it his boast that he was Somerset's friend. Now he was regent and need be servile to no one. Since that day when, in the great hall of Hampton Court, he had been made Duke of Northumberland and promptly thereafter had ordered the arrest of Somerset and his wife, he had become elated with the heady feeling of power. He intended to hold onto it. If Edward's precarious health should take a turn for the worse, he, omnipotent Northumberland, was going to need Jane Grey!

He was loud in his protestations of being a Reformist. He posed as a rabid Lutheran, though at heart he was a Catholic. Neither he nor any of the people around him were sincere religionists, but they used religion as a means to achieve their own selfish ends. Having greedily shared in the plunder of the monasteries when King Henry had outlawed Catholicism, they feared, as had Somerset, that should it be re-established, they would be stripped of a good portion of their wealth. So they posed as Reformists, and innocent little Jane might be extremely useful one day, especially since the King so plainly admired her.

"How old are you, My Lady?"

"Fifteen, sir."

"Ah, the same age as the King. I understand that you are not betrothed."

"No, sir. My betrothal to the Earl of Hertford was broken, and I am not eager to marry."

"I have five sons. As you know, my son Robert is married to Amy Robsart. But his brother Guilford is only a few years older than Your Ladyship. With your permission, I shall bring him to call one day."

"Sir, my parents will be honored," she replied modestly.

"I am a busy man, but I shall arrange it. Now I must go. I beg Your Ladyship to remain only a few minutes more. His Majesty's strength must not be taxed."

"I promise to leave soon, Your Grace. I am grateful for this time with him." She rose and curtsied to the duke, who bowed low, first to her, then to Edward, and backed out of the room.

"You won't like Guilford Dudley," Edward said when the two were alone again. "He's insufferable. Northumberland, though, loves him more than any of his other sons."

"Yes, I know," said Jane. "We met last year, and neither of us liked the other."

"But I do suppose it is time you were betrothed, Jane," Edward continued thoughtfully.

"Oh, I think there is no hurry about that. Think how old Mary is, and she is not affianced. And there's Bess. She's older than I and she's not betrothed, either. Edward, I think it's wrong to marry without love."

"Neither of us can expect such a blessing," he said, smiling wryly.

"I was content to marry the Earl of Hertford because I thought that in time I might come to care for him; but Edward, why shouldn't you and I marry for love?"

"That's a silly question."

"No. Your father married for love. With the exception of Anne of Cleves, he chose his wives because he loved them, not for reasons of state."

"We are not as strong as he was. He never had to endure a regent. When he became king, he was king in reality. It's different now. From the way Northumberland spoke, I have a feeling he's considering you for his son."

"Oh, no, I hope not!"

"From a worldly standpoint, marriage with the son of the regent would be a good match."

"If Northumberland should urge it, my parents would agree, but I—" She broke off as the doctor entered and told her it was time for the King to take his rest.

Having noted the affection in Edward's eyes when he looked at Jane, Northumberland believed that the King would be receptive to the idea which, at the proper moment, he meant to propose. And that time, from all appearances, would not be long postponed, for the doctors had told Northumberland in secret that the King was suffering from tuberculosis and that a cure was doubtful. In all probability Edward would never live to assume the full responsibilities of the crown.

John Dudley, Duke of Northumberland, was a mercenary man. There was only one person in all the world whom he truly loved, his fourth son, Guilford. If he could bring about a marriage between Jane and Guilford, and if he could force or persuade Edward to name Jane as his successor, not only would Guilford rule jointly with Jane, but Northumberland would continue as the real power in the kingdom. That was his plan. Yes, to join Lord Guilford to a lady of the blood royal was greatly to be desired.

There were, of course, two who stood in the way to the throne—Mary and Elizabeth. With regard to Mary, that sickly spinster, he anticipated no trouble. He had already planned how to deal with her when the time came.

Then there was Elizabeth, an entirely different type, lively and strong-willed. Now almost nineteen, Elizabeth would not require a regent, therefore she, too, must be dispensed with. The lives of Mary and Elizabeth must end on the block. That is, if Edward died. For the present, Northumberland realized the wisdom of keeping his daring, unscrupulous plans to himself. After all, despite the doctors, Edward might recover.

When it began to be whispered that the King was suffering

from a fatal illness, many nobles and their ladies made pilgrimages to Beaulieu, confident that Mary would soon be their sovereign. They paid her a new kind of homage that did not for a moment deceive her. Everyone now fell upon one knee before addressing her.

Somerset, after a brief reprieve and even readmittance to the council, had again fallen victim to Northumberland's superior power and was condemned to death on obviously trumped-up charges. Edward was persuaded to sign the death decree, and his former protector was beheaded in 1552. The now widowed Duchess of Somerset, who had caused Queen Dowager Catherine so much discomfort, could no longer boast of being the first peeress in the land. As for the Dowager Lady Seymour, mother of two ill-fated sons, Thomas and Edward, and grandmother of King Edward, she was ill with a malady soon to prove fatal.

The Warning

In July, Jane, with her parents and her sister Catherine, went to Beaulieu, Mary's principal country seat, for a visit. Beaulieu was a huge Gothic mansion with three tall turrets and a fine cherry orchard. No wonder Mary loved this place, with its beautiful chapel, broad staircase, magnificent furniture, Turkish carpets, inlaid bedsteads, and Florentine brocade hangings. In the daytime there was hawking, tennis, and hunting; in the evenings, card playing and dancing. Always before bedtime there were prayers.

Though Mary and Jane were no longer so close, Jane was always sorry to leave Beaulieu and return to Suffolk Place in Southwark, that impressive new residence of the Greys where, despite the fact that she was now a young lady of fifteen, her parents continued to abuse her. Besides, she was sure to meet Northumberland, who was a frequent caller and who bombarded her with questions about Mary. She was afraid of him, though as yet he had given her no overt cause to be. His wife, an officious woman, adored him. She always treated Lady Jane with sharpness and Jane thoroughly disliked her.

The girl knew that Northumberland had done much to foster the enmity between the Seymour brothers, that he had worked underhandedly to depose Somerset, in spite of the fact that in June, 1550, he had negotiated the marriage between Somerset's youngest daughter, Anne, to one of his sons, John, Viscount Lisle and Duke of Warwick. And now seemed a propitious time to bring about another marriage—that of his favorite, Guilford.

He permitted Mary to pay a brief visit to her brother at Westminster early in 1553 and agreed that Lady Frances should be part of her train. In March, shortly after the Princess had returned to Beaulieu, it became evident that Edward could not live much longer, though Northumberland caused the report to be circulated that the King was recovering.

Speaking rapidly and decisively, he now confided his plans to Jane's parents.

"I have always disliked Mary and Elizabeth," he confessed. "If I can prevent it, neither of them will become queen."

They gasped. This, if repeated, amounted to treason.

"The King," Northumberland continued, "is failing fast."

"I noticed his dry cough and his weakness," said Henry guardedly. "I, together with Cranmer, have watched him anxiously. He seemed to take a turn for the worse after Somerset's death."

Now Northumberland revealed his plan. Marry Guilford and Jane. Well, the Greys had no objection to that. Jane was sixteen, Guilford a few years older. But when Northumberland said he intended to make Jane queen, they listened with consternation.

"How can such a plan possibly succeed?" asked Lady Frances.

"And what about Princess Mary, Your Grace?" queried Henry.

"I beg you not to worry about her," he reassured them. "She can do nothing. I have my own army. True, they are mostly mercenaries whom I have brought from France, but that is all the better for my purpose. They will have no feeling of loyalty to Mary or Elizabeth. As for those two, they'll find themselves in the Tower before anyone knows about it. I have planned everything down to the most minute detail."

Philip II of Spain, husband of Queen Mary:
Titian. National Gallery, Naples

Lady Frances Grey, Duchess of Suffolk,
and her second husband, Adrian Stokes: Hans Eworth

To the Greys, the idea of having their daughter on the throne was dazzling, but there was a terrific risk involved. They carefully refrained from speaking.

"I have noticed your daughter closely," went on Northumberland. "She does not seem to be ambitious."

"No," said Lady Frances. "The girl is docile, gentle, and has always been obedient. Though she has no desire to be queen, she will cause no trouble, depend upon it. But, Your Grace, can you hope to set aside the claims of Mary and Elizabeth without the consent of the council?"

"I have thought of everything," Northumberland assured them. "Have no fear. Everything will be entirely legal. Guilford is the only one of my sons who is still a bachelor. Besides, he and Jane are the proper ages. All will be well."

Northumberland had expected no trouble from Henry Grey, whom he considered a weakling, even while recognizing the value of his friendship.

"This winter," he went on, "my family and I will go to Sion and you will go to Sheen. There we will play chess and, since the castles are almost opposite each other, the young people will have a chance to become acquainted. Meanwhile, you will invite my wife, my son, and me to a private dinner here on Wednesday."

The castles of Sion and Sheen to which he referred had formerly belonged to Somerset. After his death Sion House had been appropriated by Northumberland, while Sheen had been given to Henry Grey. It was a large building with a Gothic gallery and was supposed to be haunted. Ghostly whisperings were heard, hurrying footsteps, the flutter of silken garments.

After the regent left, the Greys sat in troubled silence. They agreed that since Northumberland was in power, they themselves would have increased prestige if Jane married his son, though they had no liking for Guilford. It was the proposal to make Jane queen that they found at once dazzling and dangerous. They decided not to mention it to Jane.

At the dinner party on Wednesday, only the Dudleys and the Greys were present, and the elders saw to it that the two young people were left alone after dinner.

"It's good news that the King is improving," Jane said after a long, chill pause, politely trying to mask her antagonism.

"Yes." Guilford stood at the far end of the room. "You know, I suppose, why they have left us alone like this?"

"No, I—"

"Come," he said rudely, "you're not quite a fool. They're determined upon our marriage. Haven't you been told about that?"

"No! Oh, no!"

"Your Ladyship seems shocked at the idea."

"I am. Is there nothing we can do to prevent it? I don't know you, but I'm sure I could never love you."

"That's true for me, too. You don't appeal to me at all. At least we can be honest with each other, My Lady."

"I must see His Majesty! I shall beg him not to agree to this!"

"On his doctor's orders, visitors are denied him. No, we must go through with it whether we like it or not."

"I won't! I won't!"

She turned from him and entered the room where Northumberland and Henry Grey were playing chess before a glowing fire. The two men's wives were chatting.

Jane walked directly to her father, her eyes glittering angrily. "Is it true, sir, that you intend that Lord Guilford and I shall marry?"

Astonished at this show of temper, her father rose and glared at her. "It is true, and you should rejoice in so fine a match."

"No! My heart is plighted elsewhere!"

"You mean the Earl of Hertford?"

This was not what she meant, but she did not choose to reveal that it was Edward to whom her heart, if not her hand, had long been plighted.

"The troth with Lord Hertford is over," said Lady Frances, coming toward her daughter threateningly.

"I will not marry Lord Guilford!" Jane cried.

Her father struck her and she reeled backward, dizzy from the blow, clutching a table for support. "This marriage," he lied, "has been decreed by the King. Do you intend to disobey the King as well as your father?"

"Decreed by the King?" She could not believe that. Her heart was throbbing wildly, her head was swimming. "Even so, I will not marry Lord Guilford! I prefer to marry the earl."

"What good would such a marriage do you now that Somerset is gone?" asked the Duchess of Northumberland sharply. "You are a fool, My Lady."

"Madame, I will never be a wife to your son!"

The duchess smiled. "Marry him. Whether you are a real wife to him or not depends upon yourself. Come, let us have no more of this. After you are married, you shall have your own establishment. I will take my son home with me. Meanwhile, we will spend the winter at Sion and your family will be at Sheen. There you and Guilford will have an opportunity to know one another better."

"I must see the King! I must speak to him!"

"He is permitted no visitors," said Northumberland.

Her father slapped her again. "Go to your room. You will marry as I choose. And if you dare defy me again, by my faith, I'll teach you better manners!"

She left the room, her head held high and defiantly, but common sense told her that rebellion was futile. They would beat her into submission. She had only one consolation—the duchess' promise that after marriage she would not have to live with Guilford but would have her own establishment.

A week later the two families left for the country. No sooner had they arrived than Lady Frances and the duchess began on Jane's trousseau, not consulting her, but calling in a steady stream of Italian silk merchants, glovers, milliners, and embroiderers.

If their parents expected that the two young people, as neighbors, would come to like each other better, they were disappointed. Jane pointedly avoided Guilford, and when they did meet he was unfailingly rude.

One day as Lady Frances and Henry were strolling in the gallery discussing this, they suddenly seemed to see a skeleton arm and hand thrust out of the wall in front of them.

"It is holding a sword dripping with blood!" Lady Frances screamed, her face pallid. "It means death!" she now whispered. "Death."

"Death to whom?" her husband asked shakily.

There was no reply—only an increase of ghostly murmurings. The entire gallery seemed peopled with unseen presences, sighing and sobbing.

"This is nonsense," Henry asserted, assuming a bravado he was far from feeling. "We imagined it." He felt of the wall. "See, now, how solid. Solid stone."

"Death," Lady Frances muttered, swaying as though she were about to faint. "A sword dripping with blood! Death to us all."

"I tell you, we imagined it. Look on the floor. There are no bloodstains. Come, we'll go down into the great hall. We'll summon the minstrels and musicians, light every candle. Why should we tremble? We have naught to fear. Northumberland rules the realm. We shall soon be united with him by marriage. Our daughter will sit on the throne. It is all arranged. What have we to fear?"

Lady Frances tremulously agreed that apparently they had no cause for fear. She said they must not mention this weird apparition to anyone.

"We cannot break this troth," she muttered more to herself than to him.

"And why should we?" he queried in an agitated tone. "I tell you, we have everything to gain by it and naught to lose!"

Edward

After this disturbing experience the Greys were eager to leave Sheen and return to London, but the Northumberlands wished to remain in the country a few months longer. As the days passed, Lady Frances became more irritable, and as usual her eldest daughter bore the brunt of her tensions.

No one seemed to find it reprehensible that Guilford should treat his affianced rudely, ignoring her as much as possible, but Jane's arms were sore from the pinchings she received because she persisted in trying to avoid her fiancé.

"Smile at him . . . talk to him . . . ask him to go for a walk . . ."

Her parents could not understand her aversion to the boy, for he was invariably polite to adults. He knew how to bow, to dance, to play tennis, and he was fastidious in his attire. He was tall, slender, with a fair complexion, light brown hair, and brown eyes. Most girls found him attractive.

"What else does Your Ladyship want in a husband?" Lady Frances would ask in a tone of exasperation. "Every other girl in the realm would accept him eagerly. But you! You—"

"I have no liking for him and he has none for me."

Let them slap and pinch her and push her toward the boy, she still could not force herself to pretend. She was deeply troubled, often asking herself why Edward had consented to the match. As her friend, he should have consulted her before giving his official approval: Jane, being of the blood royal, could not marry without his consent.

Had they lied to him and told him that she wanted to

marry Guilford? If only she could see him! But despite her
anguished pleas, Northumberland insisted that this was impossible. Knowing that she heartily disliked his son, he feared
that if she saw Edward she would beg him to withdraw his
consent, and Edward, being boyishly in love with her, would
grant her request. No, they must not meet.

Had Jane known how ill the King was, she might have understood. His eyesight had become worse. It was painful for
him to read the various documents Northumberland presented for his signature. He signed most of them because he
was too weak to read or even question them.

So when Northumberland had thrust before him the ap-
plication for Guilford's marriage to Jane, he had signed it
without reading it. There were several marriage documents
handed him at the same time—Lady Jane Grey to Lord Guilford Dudley; Lady Catherine Grey to Lord Henry Herbert,
eldest son of the Earl of Pembroke; Lady Catherine Dudley,
Guilford's younger sister, to Henry, Lord Hastings, eldest son
of the Earl of Huntington; the betrothal paper of Lady Mary
Grey to Arthur, Lord Grey de Wilton.

In March the two families returned to London. Jane had
but one thought now—to see Edward. She had written,
though she suspected that her letters were kept from him.
Almost the first thing she did upon her return to London was
to go to the palace, but she was turned away at the door.

Tearfully she pleaded with her father to arrange a meeting.

"Impossible. The King must have absolute quiet. He can
see no one. Anyhow, you would beg him to break your troth.
That would be an insult to the Duke of Northumberland.
Are you so stupid that you don't realize that none of us can
afford to do that?"

"I will not marry Guilford Dudley!"

"I'll have no disobedience in my house. It is time you
were married. There is no better match in England."

Jane asked in a low, tremulous voice what date her parents had set for the wedding and was told that it was May 21.

"But that's only two months off!"

"Exactly. Your sister Catherine will be married on the same day, as well as Guilford's sister Catherine. Thus we shall save on the cost."

"Your Grace, I beg you, don't force me to marry! I can never love Guilford."

"Love! What a romantic fool you are! Does your sister Catherine make such a fuss? She is not enamored of her bridegroom either, but she behaves like a sensible girl."

"Will—will the King be present at the wedding?"

"It is improbable. Why can't you be reasonable about this?"

"I would rather die than marry Guilford!"

"Marry him you must. Better reconcile yourself to it. His father is determined upon the marriage, and I could not prevent it even if I wished."

"But why? Why has Northumberland chosen me as a wife for his son? There are many other girls who would feel honored. Why me?"

Henry's thin mouth tightened. "He has his reasons," he replied evasively.

It did not occur to Jane what those reasons might be.

As each passing day brought the time for her marriage closer, she became increasingly nervous and depressed. Even up to the day preceding the event, she went to her father and insisted brokenly that she be permitted to see the King.

"Listen, now," he said in a tone of exasperation. "You cannot see him. Edward is dying."

This was a blow that left her quivering. Her own problem was instantly forgotten. She could not face such tragic news.

"No," she cried, "no!"

"It must not be generally known, but there is no hope for his recovery. Edward may die any day, any minute."

She had no will to resist now. Completely unnerved, on the verge of prostration, she went to her room, sobbing. Suddenly what was happening to her became unimportant. Edward dying! She could not believe it, could not face it.

All about her the big house was abustle with preparations for the wedding feast and the betrothal announcement of little Mary to one of their kinsmen. It was to be the most elaborate affair of the social season. Princess Mary had agreed to be present. Princess Elizabeth had not been invited.

Followed by white-robed bridesmaids, preceded by musicians, the three brides were led to the Dudley private chapel, wearing gowns of gold embroidery, their hair hanging in braids. It was May 21, 1553. Jane was sixteen. Edward was too ill to come, but Lady Frances had told her daughters that he had sent them many jewels and much costly plate. Actually, using the King's money, Northumberland had purchased the gifts and sent them in Edward's name.

Jane endured the wedding rehearsal and the wedding itself like an automaton. Seldom did her mind leave the sickroom at Westminster. She wondered how everyone could seem so happy when Edward was dying.

Following the ceremony there was a return to Suffolk Place, which was decorated lavishly with May flowers and crowded with richly dressed nobility. Somehow, Jane managed to go through with the festivities, her thoughts centered solely upon Edward.

When the day ended she was escorted to Chelsea Manor, which now belonged to Northumberland. Guilford returned to his own home. Catherine went to Pembroke House with her bridegroom, and Lady Mary was sent back to Bradgate. Princess Mary returned to Beaulieu, and Mrs. Ellen said that she had heard that King Edward had been taken to the royal castle at Greenwich, a village near London.

At Chelsea Manor, Jane collapsed. Free from the society of her husband, free from the domination of her parents, she wandered like a small, weeping ghost through the rooms where she had once been so happy. Catherine's bedchamber with its many cushions. How Catherine had loved cushions! The fishpond where she, Bess, Catherine, and Lord Thomas had so often sat in the early evenings. The postern gate through which, while their marriage was still secret, the Queen Dowager had admitted her husband.

But most of the time Jane spent in bed. She had few visitors. Her husband never called. Lying there in Catherine's bed, the thought came to Jane that she, too, had been poisoned, for she could not otherwise explain her strange illness and debility. Actually, her condition was caused by the strain she had been under, coupled with the knowledge that Edward was leaving her.

Directly after the wedding, Northumberland had gone into action, knowing that he now had little time to lose. During the marriage ceremonies and the feast that followed it, there had been guarded whisperings against him. He was not deaf to them, but they failed to warn him. The following day, as he entered the royal sickroom at Greenwich, he was a confident, self-satisfied man. He had decided not to mention the fact that Jane was now the bride of his son.

Edward looked very ill. Clearly, death could not be far off. Instead of compassion, Northumberland felt a thrill of expectancy. For years he had worked and schemed, and now at last the crown was practically in his hands.

"The King's Grace seems better today," he began, assuming a light tone.

The King turned his head away.

"I fear I must talk to Your Majesty of a serious matter," Northumberland continued.

He paused, sure of the outcome, relishing its accomplishment. He had won a powerful peer, the Earl of Huntington, to his side by marrying his own daughter, Catherine Dudley, to the earl's eldest son. The help of Sir William Herbert, the Earl of Pembroke, Catherine Parr's brother-in-law, was assured by the marriage of Jane's sister Catherine to Lord Pembroke's son. The army, fortresses, and foreign soldiers were at Northumberland's command. France had hinted that she would support him. He had overlooked nothing. All that remained was to finish this business with Edward.

"I know, my liege, that you are much attached to"—he was careful not to mention her by her new name—"to the Lady Jane Grey."

A flicker of interest lit up Edward's dull, sunken eyes. "Jane. Jane. Where is Jane? Why can't I see her? I command you to bring her to me!"

"Later, my liege. At present she is visiting in the country. She has written the King's Grace several times, professing her love and loyalty, but because of your illness I thought it best not to give you her letters. The doctors have said that Your Majesty must be spared any excitement. And speaking of the Lady Jane, there is a grave matter which we must consider today."

"I am too weary, Your Grace."

"I crave Your Majesty's attention. If—oh, may God forbid it!—but if Your Majesty should die, it behooves us to consider the succession."

"I can do nothing about that. It is ordained by my father's will. He decreed that anyone who attempts to change that will is to be accounted a traitor. Princess Mary will succeed me."

"An unpleasant prospect, sire. The people would rise in arms against it. England might be plunged into civil strife. I doubt that the King's Grace would wish that. I also doubt that Your Majesty would want to see the country become Catholic."

"No! No!"

"Yet it certainly would, my liege, if the crown is ever placed on the head of Princess Mary."

"I know. However, there is nothing I can do about it, nothing."

"I make so bold as to differ with Your Majesty. There is something you *can* do. There is a way, wholly legal, by which Your Majesty can save his country. Everyone knows how eager the Princess Mary is to restore her religion. We must consider that alone now. You know, sire, and I know, and the council knows that the Princess will refuse to comply with our desire to maintain the present religion."

"Yes. Well? I am very tired, Your Grace. Come to the point."

"We know, too," went on Northumberland imperturbably, "that she will at once free those whom we have justly put in the Tower, people who are our enemies. It is imperative that we prevent this."

"Have done, Your Grace! I am willing, if I could, to put Mary aside. In that case the crown would go to Bess, who is a Protestant."

Northumberland had anticipated this. Elizabeth, now twenty, would at once reign in her own right. If he were to maintain his position as the sole power in England, he must eliminate Elizabeth.

"True; but Your Majesty's affection for his sister Elizabeth no longer exists. As a matter of fact, sire, you have as much right to settle the succession as your royal father had."

"I? I have the right? Are you sure?"

"Permit me to recall to Your Majesty's mind certain facts. Your father passed by the offspring of his sister Margaret of Scotland and placed next in succession to Princess Elizabeth the eldest granddaughter of his younger sister, Mary. Mary, as Your Majesty is aware, became the wife of Charles Brandon. Lady Frances, Mary's child by this marriage, is, as Your

Majesty knows, not mentioned in your father's will; but her three daughters by Henry Grey—"

"I am well acquainted with these facts, sir," said Edward impatiently.

"In mentioning them I wished only to recall to Your Majesty's mind a matter of utmost importance. It is time that Your Majesty made his will. A mere formality, of course, since Your Majesty will recover from his present indisposition, but—"

"Very well. I will make a will tomorrow. Go now. I am very tired."

"I regret to say that it must be done at once. I have here a paper. Have I Your Majesty's permission to read it?"

Edward nodded.

It was a long-winded document naming Jane as his successor.

"Jane!" gasped Edward when Northumberland had finished. "Jane—queen? How can this be, Your Grace?"

"Your Majesty would like to see her queen? Your Majesty believes her to be wise and good?"

"Yes. Yes."

"Besides, she is a Lutheran. The country would not be compelled to endure the upheaval of a change. Untold lives would be spared."

"Yes."

"You will sign this will, sire? And I have your permission to lay it before the council?"

"Is it legal? With whom have you discussed this?"

"Entirely legal, sire. I have discussed it with three lawyers. It was they, in fact, who wrote it."

He neglected to say that these men had not given him an easy time. They had firmly reminded him that Henry had chosen the order of succession, that Henry's will had been verified by Parliament, and that it had been decreed at that time that anyone who tried to change the order of succession should suffer death as a traitor. They had feared for their own lives. Northumberland had threatened them, but they had remained obdurate. Next he had tried bribing them, but in this also he had failed.

Finally he had asked if they would cooperate if they had a written pardon from the King to make certain they would not be punished should they ever be accused of breaking the law. And lastly he had reminded them that if they did not agree to do as he asked, he would see to it that Edward signed their death warrants! This had proved to be the deciding factor. Northumberland now took from his doublet another paper.

"The lawyers," he continued, "require for their protection Your Majesty's signature to this separate document. A pen, sire. Sign here."

"This is merely a protection to the lawyers who have changed my father's will?"

"Yes, sire. A mere formality. Your Majesty might read it."

Difficult though it was for him, Edward read the paper and saw that it was as Northumberland had said. Then he signed it.

"And now," went on Northumberland with a smile, "for the will itself. I have already read that to Your Majesty."

"It is enough for today." Edward began to cough painfully and sank back on his pillows.

But Northumberland waited patiently until the coughing ceased. "I regret that I must continue, Your Majesty. You must understand that the Princesses Mary and Elizabeth are merely Your Majesty's half sisters and therefore *cannot* be your heirs!"

"Is that true? I never knew that!"

"It is true, I swear."

For several minutes Edward stared thoughtfully up at the ceiling.

"Jane," he muttered at last. "Jane. Yes, she would make an excellent queen. She is wondrous lovely. Yes, I wish it so. Give me the will."

Northumberland watched with secret elation as the dying youth signed. Then the regent left at once, and after doubling the guard around the sickroom, hastened to call a meeting of the council.

And so, on that morning in late May, the fate of Jane Grey was sealed. Lonely, she lay in bed at Chelsea Manor, unable to eat, unable to sleep, desperately worried about the one person she loved in the world—the young man who, unknown to her, had just given her all he had to give—the crown of England.

The Mysterious Summons

Northumberland, these days, was the busiest man in the realm. He had to prepare the official proclamation of Jane's queenship, a patent that must be signed by over one hundred nobles, but this took so long that it was incomplete by the time of Edward's death.

That Edward had named Jane to succeed him was a closely guarded secret, and Northumberland stressed the necessity for secrecy when he laid the King's edict before his colleagues in the council. Here he met with some show of resistance, but Edward's will did much to set aside the council members' scruples, especially since Northumberland insisted that by Edward's command they *must* sign it. Cranmer, the head of the council, remonstrated vigorously before putting his signature to the document. He was the last to sign; yet, having decided to do so, he did not claim later that he had been forced to sign, as most of the other peers did.

Northumberland, visualizing nothing ahead but triumph, was jubilant. He gave many entertainments and always invited Jane, who had an excellent excuse for not attending, her doctor having warned her that she must avoid all strain and excitement.

One day in June, while seated by the window, she was surprised to see the regent enter the courtyard accompanied by his wife, one of his daughters, his five sons, and Jane's own parents. Though scarcely able to stand, she dressed and went downstairs to receive them.

"My Lords and Ladies," she began coldly, "I am honored

by your visit. Had you given me notice of it, I would have welcomed you more fittingly."

"We have come to have a conference with Your Ladyship," announced her father-in-law.

"A conference, Your Grace? With me?"

"It is to remind you that in accord with the will of King Henry the Eighth, the crown becomes yours should his three children die without heirs."

"I am aware of that, sir." She was puzzled by this, and, still weak, sank into a chair facing them. "Tell me, how is the King? May I see him? Only for a few minutes? Oh, sir, I beg you, let me see him!"

"I regret to say that the King has taken a turn for the worse."

She gave a low moan and her eyes filled with tears. "I . . . I cannot bear to think that he may die," she murmured.

"Be steady, Jane," ordered her father sternly.

"Pray continue, Your Grace," said Lady Frances, smiling at Northumberland.

"The news we bring may startle you, My Lady," went on the regent. "But in accord with King Edward's will, should he die, you will be our queen."

"What? I?" She gazed incredulously from one face to the other, then back to Northumberland. "Not so, Your Grace. There is some mistake. The crown belongs to Princess Mary if . . . if . . . oh, God forbid! . . . if anything should happen to His Majesty."

"You will be Queen of England!" Northumberland's voice was harsh. "You must realize that. Surely you must have considered such a possibility?"

"Never! I don't want the crown!"

"You must abide by the King's will."

"King Edward wishes you to have the crown," said Lady Frances, angered that her daughter should make such an incomprehensible statement. "Not want the crown! Are you mad? Anyhow, he has made his will and named you as his successor. Do you not understand? The matter is settled!"

"It cannot be!" insisted Jane. "Mary's claim is—"

"It is your patriotic duty to accept this responsibility," declared her father. "The people do not want Mary. Besides, it is Edward's wish."

"I cannot believe this. I don't want to be queen!"

"Nevertheless," said Robert Dudley, one of Guilford's brothers, "it is your fate, My Lady. Resign yourself to it and know that we will all serve you faithfully, dying for you if necessary."

"No, no. I beg you, sirs, I plead with you! This is wrong! This is—"

"What a fool you are!" cried Guilford. "A crown is offered you, and what do you do? Turn white and tremble!"

"I have delivered King Edward's will to the council," said Northumberland sternly. "Tomorrow you are required to appear before them. My daughter and her husband will escort you. Be ready."

"This . . . this is impossible!" Jane exclaimed. "I say it again—I have no desire to be queen!"

Her mother gave her a cruel pinch on the arm. "Don't talk like an idiot!"

"I am not able to rule. I—"

"Have no fear," replied her father-in-law smugly. "I will rule for you. Be ready to face the council tomorrow morning."

Their faces blurred before her and she thought she was going to faint. Edward worse! And she a queen! It could not be. The council would surely see that it was wrong. And yet, if Edward wished it, how could it be illegal? She was bewildered and frightened. The crown surely belonged to Mary —to Mary, who had always been friendly to her.

Her visitors, showing their displeasure, quickly left. She began pacing the floor, then finally fell to her knees and prayed.

She prayed for Edward's life. She prayed that God would spare her from assuming the crown.

Finally, sick, weak, distraught, she cried out in agony, "Nevertheless, Thy will, not mine, be done!" Then she rose and went back to her bedroom. Here she sank into a chair, staring with unseeing eyes into the now quiet courtyard, trying to comprehend how she, and not Mary, could be queen. She tried to tell herself that if it was Edward's desire, then she must accept his decree.

A recognition of her youth and helplessness added to her turmoil. She tried to reason things out quietly and sensibly, but she was unable to think coherently. Edward was dying. She must be calm and reasonable. He was her King. To obey the King was her duty. Again and again she told herself this, thinking in short, clipped sentences, her nervous anxiety mounting. He was her King. It was her duty to obey him.

Moaning, she put her head in her hands. Was there rest anywhere? Was there peace? She remembered the tragic condition of her country—the poverty of the people and the vast wealth of the nobles. As queen she might bring justice. Even with this hope, she shrank from the burden of the crown, and with stark horror faced the possibility of reigning. All night she tossed, reminding herself that the throne rightly belonged to Mary—yes, no matter what Northumberland and her parents said, no matter whether Edward wanted her to be queen or not!

Dawn came, finding her wide-eyed, white, and shivering, although the June day was warm and sunny. When Mrs. Ellen brought her breakfast, the food choked her.

"Take it away."

"What did they say to Your Ladyship yesterday that troubles you so? Have they no heart in them? Couldn't they see that you are so weak you can scarcely stand?"

She could not bring herself to confide in this faithful, elderly soul.

"Bring me my clothes. I shall have to go out." Yes, there was no way to avoid it. She must face the entire council. "God," she prayed, "give me the strength to do this! Don't let me faint! Don't let me cry."

"Go out? But Your Ladyship is hardly—"

"My pink brocade gown, no jewels."

"No jewels? Very well, illustrious Lady, but"—Mrs. Ellen sighed—"but must you go out?"

"Yes, I must."

"But why? And where?"

"The council."

"The council! Why should you have to face the council?"

"Please! I beg you, don't question me!"

Rising, she found that she was quite calm, icily calm, though her knees were weak. When she was partially dressed she gazed at herself in the mirror. A queen—you? You with your freckles? You don't look like a queen. You don't know how to reign. You must refuse the crown!

Now, her mind clear, she understood why she had been married to Guilford. Even at the time of betrothal her parents and the Northumberlands must have known that she would be queen!

She thought longingly of Catherine—wise, loving Catherine, the one adult in the world whom she had trusted. If only Catherine were here to guide and sustain her! That bright spring morning Jane was crushingly aware of a profound sense of bereavement and aloneness. How deeply she needed someone to encourage and advise her, someone to whom she could turn with perfect confidence!

Never had she felt so desperately alone, so afraid, so bewildered. All her book knowledge was of no help now. She knew that none of the nobles whom she was soon to face wanted her to be queen because they believed she would be a good one. No, her elevation had nothing to do with benefiting the country. But Edward—yes, he must believe that, he alone.

If only she could have a quiet, candid talk with him! Edward—dying? Her eyes flooded with tears at the thought of losing him. Never to see Edward again? When her mind considered that possibility, anguish tore at her and everything else in the world was dwarfed to insignificance, even the ordeal that would soon confront her.

Then, because his death was too dreadful to contemplate, she began to assure herself that he would recover. Miracles could happen! He would get well. Then everything would be normal again. Despite this flash of hope, her depression was abysmal. It seemed to Jane that if Edward died she would have nothing in the world to live for.

"Oh, God, please, dear God, don't let him die!"

Noises in the courtyard brought her to the window. They were here—her husband, his parents, one of her sisters-in-law, Lady Sidney, and her mother. There they were, resplendently dressed, accompanied by a hundred soldiers. The time had come—and she had been unable to prepare herself for it.

Jane felt that she was about to lose consciousness; she could not face them. And beyond them was the royal council. Could she stand before that august body and refuse the crown? But would her refusal prevail if the King had already and in writing proclaimed her his successor? She was certain that Mary and Bess had been kept in ignorance of this matter. She considered writing them, but she knew that from now on she would be closely watched and her letters would never reach them.

A manservant entered, going through the list of nobles and their titles, adding stiltedly, "They await Your Ladyship's presence in the great hall. Your Ladyship's palanquin has been ordered by the Duke of Northumberland."

"Oh," said Mrs. Ellen, greatly alarmed, "what is happening? What will they do to you?"

Jane fought for steadiness. "A formality, nothing more." She shivered.

"You are shivering and the day is warm. Are you sure, My Lady, that you are able to go? The doctor said—"

"I *must* go," replied Jane, struggling for composure as she moved toward the door. "Don't be worried about me."

As she walked down the broad staircase, those who waited for her looked up, inspecting her shrewdly as though she were a piece of merchandise.

"Too bad she is so short and thin," said Guilford.

"Oh, as to that," replied his mother, "we will get her some heavy-soled shoes. They will make her look taller. Good morrow, My Lady."

"Are we ready?" asked Northumberland.

She nodded.

Her mother came close to her, whispering harshly in a voice that everyone could hear. "Smile! You are not being led to an execution!" And, as was her custom, she gave Jane a cruel pinch on the upper arm. Jane winced but said nothing.

"Lift up your head!" ordered Lady Frances. "Pull back your shoulders. Act like a queen!"

"Let us go," ordered Northumberland.

Jane rode alone in her litter, the other women following in theirs, the men on horseback. They moved at a stately pace through London, the people making way for them and bowing.

The council room was empty when they entered. Northumberland motioned Guilford to stand beside her. He obeyed, holding his body stiff. Her mother stood on the other side.

"Act like a queen!" she repeated commandingly, and then in a whisper, "Have you thought of what you will say?"

"I shall tell them that I will not accept the crown."

"Are you mad? Will you disgrace your family? Will you disobey the King?"

The council now filed in, led by Thomas Cranmer, Archbishop of Canterbury, who was followed by her father. She recognized them all. To her dismay, they knelt and one by one kissed her small hand. Then gravely they took their places, facing her from behind a long oak table. There was an impressive hush that lasted only a few seconds but which to Jane seemed interminable.

"My Lords," began Grey, "do we hereby acknowledge the Lady Jane as our rightful ruler after King Edward?"

"Aye," they answered without any display of enthusiasm.

"Let it be so recorded," commanded Cranmer.

"My Lords," began Jane, her voice trembling in spite of herself, "I have never, as God is my witness, sought this honor! Indeed, sirs, I am unworthy of it. I beg you to reconsider. Surely there is some error! His Majesty is still king, and even if—even if he w-were removed, I have no claim such as that of Princess Mary and Princess Elizabeth. Therefore, will Your Lordships permit me to withdraw from accepting the crown?"

She was so little, so girlish, so earnest, that they might have relieved her of the burden had not Northumberland spoken up with a voice of authority.

"We have proclaimed you as our rightful queen!"

Jane gazed helplessly about the room. Guilford's eyes held only disapproval. The Duchess of Northumberland was scowling at her. Northumberland was plainly vexed. Her mother was frowning. Her sister-in-law looked mortified. But her father, gazing at his colleagues, was smiling. He spoke smoothly, diplomatically.

"Lords of the court, as you know, my daughter has lived a virtuous, secluded, and a studious life. She is distressed by the illness of the King, whom she cherishes as her cousin and former playfellow. I beg you, therefore, let us now end this session."

The men nodded, rose, knelt again in homage. Her mother took Jane firmly by the arm and they walked out, Guilford following them, his mother and sister behind him, while the lords of the realm, including her father and father-in-law, remained kneeling.

"I am ashamed of you," whispered Lady Frances.

Once outside, Jane's escorts separated, leaving her to return to Chelsea Manor guarded by fifty soldiers. Arriving home, she went at once to bed, her body quivering, her hands icy.

"Oh, Catherine, Catherine," she sobbed, "if only you were here!"

Mrs. Ellen called the doctor, who ordered her to remain in bed, avoid all exertion, and see no one but her close attendants.

Ten days later, on July 6, 1553, England experienced a storm such as had never been seen before. There was hail and the roaring of violent wind. Trees were torn up and a church steeple was struck by lightning. The people were terrified. Many insisted hysterically that at Whitehall, Windsor, and Hampton Court they saw the ghost of Henry VIII standing on the battlements with his red cloak flowing in the wind, his stout, strong legs apart, shouting something that could not be heard above the thunder.

In the sickroom at Greenwich, the King's attendants, haggard with their long death watch, looked up at Northumberland.

"The King is dead," announced one of them.

"It must not be known for the present," commanded the regent roughly. "Let no one enter here. None of you must leave this room!"

He rushed down the stairs and, braving the tempest, rode at top speed to the council room, where, in expectation of this news, the council had already assembled.

"The King is dead!" he cried, bursting in upon them. "We must keep this secret until the time agreed upon! To prevent it from leaking out, we must all repair to Sion House."

Wily Northumberland had decided that Edward's death would not be announced to the world until Mary and Elizabeth were in his hands. His plan was to bring them, unsuspecting, to London. He could not hope to arrest them in their own castles without difficulty, for both Hunsdon and Hatfield were strongly fortified. However, once they entered the city, they would be seized and imprisoned in the Tower.

There is some suspicion that Edward took longer to die than Northumberland had expected. It is even possible that his death was hastened by giving him some sort of poison, since many of his final symptoms were not those of tuberculosis. Yet even if true, it is far from being proved that Northumberland had a hand in this act: The doctors had been dismissed and Edward's last days had been in the care of women whom we would call "quacks" today.

In any event, two messengers had probably already been sent to Mary and Elizabeth, telling them that His Majesty's condition was somewhat worse and that he was asking to see them. They were therefore commanded to hasten to London with all possible speed. As double precaution, John and Robert Dudley, two of Guilford's brothers, had been sent in person to bring Princess Mary to the city.

Shortly after Edward's death, Northumberland went to the residence of one of his daughters, Lady Sidney.

"Go at once to the Lady Jane and accompany her to Sion House."

"In this weather, Your Grace?"

"At once! Lose no time."

"But what reason shall I give for taking her there?"

"Tell her only that she must go at once to receive what is ordained for her by the King."

"Yes, Your Grace."

Even Lady Sidney did not know that the King was dead, and she was puzzled as she hurriedly prepared for the journey. Why would her father summon Jane to Sion House now?

Jane, in her room, had been permitted to get up and sit by the window for the first time since she had faced the council. She was reading the Bible when she gazed into the rain-drenched court and saw that she had a visitor. Lady Sidney coming to call in such a downpour? Always neatly and tastefully dressed, that day Jane was not wearing her best clothes, but she went downstairs as she was, wondering what might be the reason for the visit.

Because the need for speed had been stressed, Lady Sidney had not used her palanquin. She had ordered her fastest horse and forty horsemen. Now, buffeted by the wind, she was standing by the fireplace, nervously attempting to dry her feathered hat.

"Your Ladyship is brave to venture forth in such weather," began Jane graciously as she entered the great hall. "Pray you, be seated. I shall send for some—"

"Your Ladyship, there is no time for sociability. The regent summons you to Sion House at once! I pray you, put on a wrap and let us go. We must travel by horseback in order to make better time."

"But can it not wait until better weather? What is it?"

"I know not the reason for the summons, My Lady. My father bade me hasten."

"Why?"

"As I said, I know not. He told me only that you are to receive what was ordained for you by the King."

"What was ordained for me by the King? What can it be?"

"Your Ladyship, I beg you, don't delay. My men-at-arms will suffice for our protection."

Fifteen minutes later they were on their way. The storm was subsiding now, but the muddy roads impeded their progress. They talked little. They had to stop overnight on the way to Sion House.

"Bad weather for traveling, ma'am," said the landlady as she showed Jane to a small, clean room.

"Yes."

"It must be something important that would bring two ladies on the road when the mud is so—"

"True, travel is difficult, and we must leave at sunrise."

"Dreadful things must be happening, ma'am."

"What do you mean?"

"Why, haven't you heard how at Windsor and Whitehall during the great storm old King Henry was seen on the battlements? Many saw him! Clear as anything! Stomping about, he was, like they say he used to do when something angered him. He was yelling something, too, but no one could hear it because of the storm. I've heard that King Edward is ill. Is it true?"

"I am sorry to say it is true—yes."

"It couldn't be that he is dead? And the old King was trying to tell us so?"

"No, no." Jane shuddered. "No, that couldn't be. The King lives. If he had died there would be trumpeters dashing along every road proclaiming the news. No, thank God, the King lives!"

"I'm glad of that. Well, good night, ma'am. Pleasant dreams."

The woman left, unaware that she had been talking to the Queen of England.

And Queen Jane, deeply puzzled by this curious summons to Sion House, fatigued by the journey, settled in her strange bed and gazed up at the ceiling through the darkness. Except that in the distance a dog barked at the quiet moon, the world was very still. Now that the storm was over, the weather had become oppressively hot.

Jane tossed restlessly, wondering what could be awaiting her at Sion House and why this journey should be such an urgent one. Edward still lived; she did no doubt that. If he had died it would surely have been made known. What could he possibly have "ordained" for her?

Dear Edward. He must be making her a present of some rare jewels. Could it be that? If so, why should she have to go all the way to Sion House to receive the gift? Then the stirring thought came to her that perhaps he had been taken to Sion House. Yes, that must be it! He was better. Soon she would see him. And she was wearing one of her plainest dresses!

She could scarcely wait for daylight to start off again.

Long Live the Queen!

After breakfast next morning, Lady Sidney and Lady Jane continued their journey. The day was Sunday, July 9. Country people stood respectfully at the sides of the roads, the men removing their hats and wondering why anyone, especially "quality," should travel at such speed in such heat.

When at last they arrived at Sion House they were astonished to learn that the castle was empty, except for the servants. Food was brought and they ate in silence. Then they were taken to two bedchambers where they combed their hair and washed. Later, when they met in the great hall, there was nothing to do but sit down and wait.

"I had hoped the King might be here," said Jane.

"No," replied Lady Sidney, "I'm sure His Majesty is too ill to travel."

A few minutes later the nobles began to arrive, accompanied by their ladies. They did not enter the great hall but remained in a large room, waiting for the rest of their numerous party.

"This is very odd," said Jane. "Should we not go to greet them?"

"Depend upon it, the servants have told them that we are here. I think it best to wait where we are. My father gave me no further directions. This whole thing is very strange." Lady Sidney was standing at the long window. "Ah, here comes my family. Guilford isn't with them. I wonder why?"

"Your brother has no desire to see me, nor I to see him," answered Jane.

"I admit Guilford is rather difficult. My father was always strict with the rest of us, but he was soft and indulgent where Guilford was concerned. Still, no matter what kind of person Guilford is, you are his wife and you will certainly have to make the best of it. Ah, here is the Bishop of Winchester. This must be an important meeting, a most important one."

"Mysterious, too. Why should there be such a congregation so far from London?"

"We shall soon know."

About fifteen minutes later the big double doors were thrown open and in stately procession the lords and their ladies entered, led by the Duchess of Northumberland and the Duchess of Suffolk, Jane's mother. To Jane's dismay, they all knelt before her. Confused, she waited for someone to speak.

Northumberland rose. "The King is dead," he announced. "Long live the Queen!"

"Long live the Queen!" echoed the others.

Jane gasped. She had heard only the first sentence—"The King is dead." Her knees became weak and her heart pounded crazily.

"By an act of our late King Edward," went on Northumberland, "anyone who recognizes Princess Mary and Princess Elizabeth as having any claim to the throne will be considered a traitor. By His Majesty's will you are his heir, our liege lady, to whom we now swear loyalty and obedience."

"We swear loyalty and obedience to Queen Jane," the others said solemnly.

To Jane the room seemed suspended in midair and the floor floated beneath her. Her face paper-white and drawn with sorrow, she listened as one by one each noble stepped forward, knelt, and vowed to shed his blood for her. She seemed stunned. When the tedious ceremony ended, she quietly sank to the floor in a faint.

No one made a move toward her. The swoon lasted only

a few minutes. Opening her eyes, she found herself still on the floor, the nobles staring down at her as though she were behaving badly. "The King is dead." The words echoed through her mind as she sat up. Sobbing violently, she rose to her knees.

"Oh, God," she prayed, "guide and deliver me!"

Someone helped her to her feet. The people stood, all eyes upon her, obviously waiting for her to speak.

"My Lords," she began brokenly, "I am overcome with grief. The King is dead and I grieve for him. Again I urge you to reconsider! I am weak. I have no power to govern this land, but if what you give me—the crown itself—if this be legally mine, then I will turn to God and fervently, humbly beg Him to give me grace and wisdom that I may rule the country to His glory!"

"So be it," said Northumberland, smiling broadly. "Long live the Queen!"

"Long live the Queen!"

The secret ceremony was now completed. There was no time to linger at Sion House. Jane was immediately conducted to a closed litter and the return journey to London started. Again the country people stood gaping at the sides of the road, but none of them knew that their new queen was passing. The cavalcade moved solemnly to a landing place on the Thames, where the royal party was transferred to ornate barges. The weather was fine, and everyone but Jane was in a hilarious mood.

Jane was still sobbing. Her mother kept telling her sharply to control herself.

"A queen in tears!" scoffed Lady Frances.

"Edward is dead. How can they laugh?"

Her mother did not reply.

"Where are we going?" asked Jane after a pause of several minutes.

"To the Tower, of course. Surely Your Majesty knows that

it is the custom that sovereigns go forth from the royal apartment in the Tower on the day of their coronation."

Jane moaned and sank back upon the richly upholstered couch. "And—and when will that be, Your Grace?"

"As soon as possible. Your Majesty must compose herself. I have brought along some fresh clothing that Your Majesty will don before we arrive. What kind of queen is this with a nose all red and swollen from weeping?"

"Do the people know that Edward is dead?"

"Not yet. They will know when you are conducted to the royal apartment."

"Do they want me to be queen?"

"What do the people have to do with this?" Lady Frances asked hotly. "Stop crying! You are no longer a child."

"Edward is dead," Jane answered. "I loved him so!"

When at last the royal barge and its resplendent escorting barges were made fast to the dock, a group of dignitaries, including the Lord Mayor of London and the governor of the Tower and his aides, fell to their knees. It was about three o'clock in the afternoon of July 10. A thin, graceful girl with delicate features, large hazel eyes, very white teeth, and freckles stepped forth wearing an elaborate green velvet gown and a white coif. She wore a curious pair of slippers that the Duchess of Northumberland had had made with soles three inches thick, to hid the fact that Jane was so small.

"How can I walk in these?" Jane asked.

"You must. The length of your gown will hide them. They will make you look taller. Come now, Your Majesty must not tarry."

"Pinch your cheeks to get some color in them," ordered Lady Frances. "We cannot have you looking like a ghost."

There was a blare of trumpets as she walked under the royal canopy, with her mother carrying her train.

Guilford, richly dressed in white and gold, stepped to her

side. With the nobles and their ladies following, the new Queen and her consort were conducted to the lavish apartment that had been hurriedly cleaned to receive her. Jane sat down upon a large chair.

The room was crowded with people—her father's brothers, Lord John and Lord Thomas Grey, her numerous in-laws, her immediate family, and seemingly countless others. Again, dizzily, she saw them kneel, heard them swear allegiance to her, and again there came the rousing cry, "Long live the Queen!" She noticed that when they moved away from her they walked backward.

Stephen Gardiner, Bishop of Winchester, left the room but soon returned, bearing the crown on a red velvet cushion with gold tassels. Behind him were several pages carrying large boxes. "My Lord?" Jane asked quietly.

His voice and his smile were obsequious. She recalled how this man had tried to destroy Catherine Parr.

"Your pardon, Majesty." He sank to his knees, then rose and moved toward her, carrying himself with a servile stoop. "I have here the collection of jewels that belonged to King Henry's six wives, also the royal regalia. Your Majesty will be pleased to select what jewels she wishes."

"I have my own jewels, My Lord. They will suffice for the present."

"As the Queen's Grace desires. But here is one ornament which Your Majesty cannot well dismiss: the crown. I am come to see how it fits Your Majesty's head."

"Oh, no! No, I don't wish to—"

"The Queen may take it boldly, fearlessly. It belongs to the Queen's Highness. I wish at this time only to try it on in order to make sure of its fit. Perchance it should be made a trifle smaller or larger. Permit me, Madame."

He put the crown on her head. It felt too large and heavy. She quickly removed it, handing it back to him.

"I shall have another made to crown your husband with,"

he said in that subservient tone which she found so annoying.

"What? It seems, sir, you take your orders from the Duke of Northumberland!"

"It is to be a joint rule!" said Guilford huffily. "The Queen's Grace must have known that!"

"I did not know it and I will never agree to it. You are unfit to rule!"

"You will do as you are told," Guilford burst out. "You did not want to marry me, and now when you are made queen by my father's power, you try to prevent me from ruling!"

"My Lord, there is naught to be gained by such outbursts. If you would be king, you must be made so by the Parliament and with my consent."

"My father will take care of this matter," cried Guilford. "He has told me that eventually you will be merely queen consort and I shall be king! He is master in England!"

"I may retire, Your Majesty?" asked Gardiner smoothly.

She nodded, rose from the chair, and both men sank to their knees as she left the room.

That night, despite her weariness, she lay in bed remembering that King Henry and Edward had occupied the same bed when they had been escorted to the Tower to remain in traditional seclusion prior to their coronation. She thought, too, how eagerly her mother, her mother-in-law, her sisters, and Guilford's sisters must be even now preparing for the event. But the new Queen wished that morning might never come.

She was awakened next day by Mrs. Ashley and Mrs. Ellen, both of them tremulous with elation, yet somewhat dazed. Mrs. Ellen said that they had brought her clothing and jewels from Chelsea Manor. Jane, feeling inexpressibly tired, as though she had not slept at all, longed to remain in bed, but after she had been served breakfast she was told that she must rise and dress, for her husband and his mother were already waiting in the anteroom to see her.

The Queen was still in the process of being dressed when they entered. Their conduct was vastly different from the homage they had shown her the night before. There were no bows. Guilford's eyes were bright and impertinent as he haughtily ordered Jane's servants out of the room.

"You are my wife," he exclaimed wrathfully. "I demand that I be treated as your husband!"

"Yes, Jane," said the duchess in a tone of authority. "Guilford is right. Henceforth you must be a real wife to him."

"Never! I will never let him touch me!"

"Remember, it is my husband who has put you where you are. Since you are not of an age to rule, he is still regent. And as for ruling, you are not to reign alone, you know. Guilford will share your throne and bear the title of king." She gazed adoringly at her son.

"The crown is not a plaything for boys and girls," answered Jane decisively. "I can make my husband a duke, but only Parliament can make him a king."

The duchess began pacing back and forth angrily. "Guilford will be king!" she retorted. "He will be king!"

Then, to Jane's astonishment, Guilford burst into tears and flung himself out of the room, slamming the door.

"You are an ungrateful wife!" shouted the duchess, and she, too, flounced out of the room.

No sooner had Jane finished dressing than they were back, subjecting her to another unpleasant scene. Despite their raised voices, she remained adamant. Once again, taking her son by the hand this time, the irate duchess left the room, declaring that Jane was stubborn and ungrateful and that Guilford would leave her forever and reside at Sion.

Dreading another such scene, Jane decided to discuss the matter with someone who, she hoped, would give her an impersonal opinion. Who? The first names that came to her mind were those of the Earl of Arundel and Sir William Herbert, Earl of Pembroke. She sent for them.

When they arrived, she repeated calmly what Guilford and his mother had said and how she had answered them.

"We approve of Your Majesty's decision. Pray, Your Majesty, leave this matter to us."

When they had gone she wondered whether it had been wise to ask their advice, for the Earl of Arundel was supposedly one of Northumberland's closest friends.

Braving the wrath of the regent, the two men went at once to Guilford, whom they found pouting in the garden.

"As members of the council, sir," they began, after the usual formal bows, "we inform you that you are not to leave the Tower, at least until after the coronation of Her Majesty." The men turned and left.

Guilford sulked. Who were they to order him about? Wasn't his father regent? His father would see to it that he shared the throne, for his father had never denied him anything. Besides, he had been told clearly that in making Jane queen, his father had intended that he should bear the title of King Guilford. But perhaps he had better try to be a bit more courteous to his wife. Perhaps it would be well to apologize.

Jane, somewhat relieved by the fact that the peers had sided with her about Guilford's becoming king, was still troubled by doubts about her succession to the throne. She wondered if Mary knew what had happened in London and how she felt about it. Knowing Mary so well, Jane did not believe that the Princess would accept the present situation without some sort of protest. But what could she do?

As she was musing upon this, Guilford appeared at the doorway but did not enter the room.

"Come in, Guilford," she said, no longer angry.

He began stiffly, "I came to say . . . that is, I . . ."

"Guilford," she broke in when he paused, obviously at a

loss for words, "it is not our fault that we are married. I would rather be friends than enemies."

"I, too."

"What we have done, we did in obedience to our parents. I don't like quarreling. I hope that in the future we may— though we will never love each other—still I hope we may be . . ."

"Yes," he said, "perhaps we may learn to be friends."

The bickering, animosity, and excitement, coupled with the intensity of her grief over the death of Edward, brought on a relapse. Mrs. Ellen put Jane to bed and called the doctor. There was nothing he could do for her. Again he stressed that she needed quiet, that she must avoid all strain and remain in bed at least until the coronation.

The next few days passed quietly. Jane was introduced to Sir John Cheke, the secretary of state. She recognized him as one of Edward's former tutors and knew him to be a good and scholarly man. Northumberland presented her with letters to foreign rulers, and she obediently signed them. "The Queen's proclamation" was read to small groups of sullen and silent Londoners; Jane had had nothing to do with this document, which had also been prepared by Northumberland.

Mary

Meanwhile, several days earlier, Princess Elizabeth had received Northumberland's message to come to London to see Edward. To a less sophisticated mind, it would have contained nothing to cause suspicion: Her brother was worse and wanted to see her. She must leave immediately.

But Elizabeth's shrewdness matched that of Northumberland. Instead of ordering her maids to begin packing and commanding her men-at-arms to saddle the horses in all speed, she sat down and thought about the situation.

For a long time Northumberland had seen to it that she was kept away from Edward. Why, then, should he suddenly insist that she proceed in haste to the city? She mistrusted the duke, knowing him to be greedy, cruel, utterly unscrupulous. What to do? Disobey? She could scarcely do so without a good reason. Bess would have made an excellent actress. Instead of hurrying to London, she went to bed, pretending to be seriously ill, and sent Northumberland's weary messenger back to him with a polite letter saying that she was unable to travel.

Less warily, Princess Mary had received the identical message. Though suffering with another cold, she was touched by the information that her brother, gravely ill, wished to see her.

She was, of course, well aware of the fact that should he die, the crown would automatically be hers. It seemed to Mary that she had waited a long time for the crown. As queen, she would have the opportunity to re-establish what she was convinced was the only true religion. She envisaged the monasteries rebuilt, the priests living in safety, the people brought back into the fold of the Catholic Church.

Go to London? Ah, with all haste! So, attended by her ladies and a large escort of men-at-arms, Mary Tudor set out for the capital, her faithful companion, Mary Browne, beside her. What a plain, mousey little person this thirty-seven-year-old Princess was—tight, colorless mouth, high forehead, sparse eyebrows.

In her mannish, unpleasant voice she commanded speed. Edward must be dying, else why would Northumberland have summoned her, especially since heretofore he had obviously tried to keep her and her young brother apart. She had no love for the regent, and when she became queen she had no intention of dealing mercifully with creatures such as he.

She recalled, as she rode along, how her father had sent for her when he was dying and had asked her to take care of Edward. Gladly would she have kept this promise, but both Somerset and Northumberland had prevented her from doing so. She knew she was unpopular with the nobles—less so with the common people—but nothing could prevent her from becoming their next ruler. Nothing. This was a matter that had been settled by her father before he died. She was not only on her way to give what comfort she could to her ailing brother, but she was at long last on her way to the throne.

In London, Northumberland's uneasiness had increased. The people were more intelligent than he had believed. He had fully expected them to accept Jane jubilantly, since the only alternative was somber, shortsighted, unattractive Mary. But in the taverns and the streets the people knew that the crown rightfully belonged to Mary. They also knew that Northumberland, in making his daughter-in-law queen, had done a dishonest thing; and they knew something else—

that they hated and suspected him and that if he continued in power they could expect nothing but more poverty, more injustice.

Waiting for Mary and Elizabeth, Northumberland's anxiety reached fever pitch. If those two remained free, they would swiftly form parties against him. When Elizabeth's letter reached him he knew at once that her plea of illness was false. Well, for the time being she had evaded his snare, but her arrest would come later. Mary had fallen into his trap, and for the present he had enough on his hands, dealing with her. Thinking her brother was still alive, she was on her way to London. He knew the road she was taking. His spies reported her progress.

He sent several messengers saying that the King was worse and begging her to hasten. Meanwhile, he stationed well-armed men at the gates of London and sent a horde of his minions to Cambridge, fifty miles northeast of the city, with orders to start a riot the minute she appeared and to burn down any house in which she took refuge, thus eliminating her and saving him the problem of sending her to death on the scaffold.

Mary, worn out with the long ride and having taken only the briefest intervals for rest and refreshment, had seen the spires of Cambridge with relief. The sight meant that she was close to her goal. How weary she was! The midsummer dust was choking her. Her cold was worse. The heat was well nigh unbearable.

She was within a few miles of Cambridge when a man who had once been her goldsmith forced his way through her guard and, panting painfully, knelt in the dust before her. She recognized him at once and motioned to her guards to release him.

"What is it?" she asked. "Is the King worse?"

"I beseech Your Highness, do not go to London! The King is dead!"

"Dead? I think you must be mistaken. Only an hour ago a message came from the duke saying His Majesty was worse and I was to hurry."

"A hoax! A trap! The King is dead, I swear it!"

Mary gasped. Dead? Then she was England's queen!

"Your Highness," the man continued, "the duke's message was a lie, a trick! Do not go to London. He will arrest you. He plans to make the Lady Jane Grey queen!"

"Jane? Queen? How can this be? Are you mad, fellow?"

"On my oath, I swear it!"

Mary hesitated, her cold and weariness forgotten. How could such a monstrous thing have happened? Her thin mouth tensed. What the man had told her was incredible; yet she had found him trustworthy in the past. Loving jewels, she had frequently ordered him to make ornaments for her. He had never lied as to the value of a gem, but he must be lying now!

True, she had never put the slightest trust in Northumberland, but surely he would not attempt a thing like this! What to do—proceed or turn back? For several minutes she remained motionless, indecisive, torn, her horse as still as if it had been carved from stone. Mechanically, she ordered the man to rise and he backed away and was lost among her many attendants.

"What does the Princess wish?" asked the captain of her guard.

"Stay a while. I must think. Let the men relax in the shade until I have made up my mind."

Mary Browne rode up close to her. "Princess, I heard what the man said. Shocking as it is, I think he speaks truly."

"He might be misinformed. The King—already dead! Dead before I started this journey? It is incredible. Jane Grey to be made queen? What, then, of my father's will?"

"It is known that Northumberland holds the council in the palm of his hand. They are all afraid of him. I beg Your

Highness, let us be wise and turn back. Or at least take refuge in Cambridge until we make certain of the truth. Lo, here comes another rider. He comes at top speed. He must have news!"

"Probably only another messenger from Northumberland."

But as the rider drew nearer Mary recognized him as a gentleman whom she had always respected. Reaching her, he leaped from his sweat-lathered horse and sank panting in the dust, removing his feathered hat.

"The King is dead. You are our rightful queen! Northumberland plans to arrest you. Turn back!"

Now she was convinced. Her followers were tired, their faces streaked with dust and perspiration. She ordered them to proceed to Cambridge where they would rest for the night. And then? What then? She must not lose her head. She must plan. She thanked the messenger and sent him back to London, warning him to keep secret what he had done.

Mary and her numerous escort took lodging for the night in a large house. Scarcely was she inside it and being served with food when the whole place became a mass of flames. Fires had been started in so many spots that escape seemed impossible. But somehow Mary and her retainers managed to get out safely, and in the barn she was given a change of clothing. Disguised as a market woman, she moved through the roaring crowd until she reached the outskirts of the town, where Mary Browne and the Princess' officers, along with several horses, had found a hiding place on a heavily wooded knoll. At once they set off into the night.

Mary's mind worked quickly. There were two courses of action open to her: cede the crown to Jane, or fight for her rights. Mary Tudor was no coward. She determined to fight. How? With what? Where could she go for safety? How could she raise an army? And how could she do it in a hurry?

She knew that Englishmen, no matter how they might feel about her personally, no matter what their religious convictions might be, believed in fair play.

She remembered, too, their hatred of Northumberland. She knew that in nearby counties there was a strong Catholic group, many of whom, in order to protect the lives of their families, were obeying the anti-Catholic laws even while they still secretly adhered to the older faith. Mary headed for Norfolk.

Following Northumberland's planned riot in Cambridge, the news was brought to him that Mary and her retainers had escaped. He experienced long hours of fear and chagrin. Where had she gone? What did she intend to do? But what *could* she do? She was a frail woman. Besides, she had little money.

He learned Mary's whereabouts when, on July 9, she sent a letter to the council proclaiming herself queen and offering pardons to all its members.

They replied in an impertinent tone, insisting that Jane was already queen. Now Mary knew that she would have to fight. She set out at once for Framlingham, a strongly fortified palace with walls eight feet thick. In addition, it had the advantage of being near the coast, in case she failed to gain her people's support and was forced to flee to the Continent.

John and Robert Dudley had reached Beaulieu, Mary's residence, only to find that she had already left for London. They caught up with her as she was on the way to Framlingham, but at this point their own men turned around and declared for Mary. The two Dudleys were saved from capture only by the speed of their horses, and they swiftly continued back to London.

Suddenly, Mary seemed indefatigable. She made rousing speeches and showed a strength and stamina that no one, least of all herself, could ever have imagined. Sitting proudly on her horse, she addressed the people, most of whom were ragged and half-starved, calling upon them to proclaim her their rightful queen, explaining what Northumberland had done. And the people rallied to her cause.

"Down with Northumberland!" they shouted. "Let us have justice! Down with Jane Grey, the usurper!"

They began arming feverishly. It was a motley assortment of people who now pledged themselves to support Mary. Their weapons were many. Those who had guns loaded them, but most of the men clutched stones, staves, swords, and daggers.

"To London! To London!" they cried as they set off for the city.

Jane, in the Tower, had felt very removed from the world. But on July 14 it suddenly closed upon her again when her father came to visit her. Though she was stronger now, Henry saw with some consternation the small figure in the enormous, heavily carved bed, her beautiful eyes sunken, her face alarmingly pale.

She had spent much of her time thinking—of Elizabeth and Mary, especially of Edward.

"My Lord," she asked, "where is Elizabeth?"

"The Princess claims to be ill at Hatfield."

"And Mary?"

He kept his eyes on the floor and tried to speak calmly. "The Princess has left her residence. She is on her way to London."

"No harm must come to her! Make this clear to the regent."

"It would seem, my liege lady, that the Princess Mary well knows how to take care of herself. It appears that she is not as friendless as Northumberland imagined. But do not be troubled. The council has sworn allegiance to you."

"What do you mean by that?"

"Your Majesty has only to rest and grow strong again. I assure you, there is naught to fear."

"Sir, speak plainly. Where is the Duke of Northumberland?"

"He is kissing Guilford again and again before leaving to fight."

"Leaving? To fight? Fight for what?"

"For you and the crown."

"Against whom?"

"Against Princess Mary and her forces."

"Her forces? What forces? Where are these forces?"

"They are advancing upon London."

"How strong are they?" She sat bolt upright. "Tell me the truth!"

"They grow stronger minute by minute. But rest easy. Northumberland also has forces. They, too, are strong. Some men have already left London, led by John and Robert Dudley."

Jane saw that her father was actually afraid, but he sought to be reassuring.

"Do not concern yourself," he said, frowning at some inner image. "What can Mary accomplish? The lords of the realm have proclaimed you queen."

"The lords of the realm! Sir, we both know they are mere weathercocks, shifting with the winds. I beg of you, let there be no bloodshed! Let me cede the crown to Mary!"

"No!" he roared. "No! I tell you, you are in no danger."

"Don't you see, sir, that without the support of the people—"

"The people!" he scoffed. "*We* are the power, *we*—the council, the regent!"

Jane was not such a fool as to believe this. She had a vivid memory of Mary—pale, small, homely, with a long nose; but Mary had an inner strength. She had proven this by stanchly clinging to her religion despite all threats to force her to relinquish it.

"Mary is stronger than you realize, Your Grace," Jane said quietly.

"Nonsense. A weak, sickly woman. But if by some miracle she wins, she'll see to it that the executioner becomes an extremely busy fellow. Yet she cannot win. On July 6 our king died. On the ninth you were proclaimed queen—legally, by the council. We have naught to fear."

"The council has accepted me—true. But why? Because Northumberland holds them in his grasp. Any dissent, and he would have sent them prisoners to the Tower. But the people, what of them? They know little about me. Will they accept me?"

"The people! The people! Stop talking about the people. They will do as they are told."

"When they learned that they had a new queen, was there rejoicing?"

"No," he admitted. "The news was received in silence."

"Do they hate me, then?"

"No, but they hate Northumberland. If they hate you it is because they believe that you and he are confederates. Now I must go. There is much to do. If Mary wins, we shall all die for this!"

He turned and walked away. No longer was he the suave, elegant courtier, but a pale and harassed man.

She gazed after him worriedly. Her father was a coward; and Northumberland, for all his bluster and arrogance, was a coward, too.

Day by day the news in London grew worse. Reports were sent from Northumberland, telling of defections from his force and asking for reinforcements. He had advanced somewhat beyond Cambridge but had suffered defeat and had had to fall back to Cambridge again. Sir Edward Hastings had been commissioned to raise an army of four thousand in Middlesex and Buckinghamshire. He had succeeded in doing this—and, having succeeded, he promptly proclaimed Mary as the rightful queen!

Northumberland had sent half a dozen ships to lie off Yarmouth, in case Mary should try to escape by water to the Continent, but on the fourteenth, about the time he was leaving London with his troops and four of his sons, the fleet declared for Mary.

This news filled the council with consternation. Several of Jane's ladies came to her and asked to be excused from service, pleading illness.

"Hastings! That traitor!" cried Guilford when he paid his wife a visit shortly after lunch. "Well, my father will know how to deal with him!"

"I want nothing to happen to Mary!" Jane cried.

"Mary!" he sneered. "Nothing to happen to Mary, indeed! Better be concerned with what will happen to us unless she is killed in the fight!"

Too excited to remain long in one place, he left almost at once. As the day dragged on, many courtiers quietly crept away.

Toward evening Cranmer and Jane's father entered her sitting room.

"You are brave, sirs," she said quietly. "It seems all the others have disappeared."

"Your Majesty has naught to fear," Cranmer told her.

"What is the news?" she asked.

"All the ships in the harbors have sworn allegiance to Mary as queen," replied Henry Grey dolefully. "She has sent out a proclamation offering rewards for the capture of Northumberland—a thousand pounds in land to any noble, five hundred pounds to any gentleman, a hundred pounds to any yeoman who will bring Northumberland to her a prisoner."

"The fact is," said Cranmer angrily, "we have Northumberland to blame for this whole thing. Edward was a minor and had no legal right to dispose of the crown."

Jane gazed at him accusingly. "You knew that at the time?" she asked in a tone of astonishment.

"We all knew it—but we chose to ignore it."

"Why didn't someone speak up?"

"Speak up?" said Grey bitterly. "Knowing Northumberland, that would have been madness."

"Legally we are all traitors, then?"

"If Mary wins," answered Cranmer, "we shall be named as such."

"If she wins! I was given to understand that the duke has a strong force."

"That remains to be proven. Most of them are mercenaries. The real English soldiers have not been paid for months. Is it any wonder that they swarm to Mary's side?"

"Is the duke still at the head of his forces?" she asked.

"Yes," replied the archbishop, "but we can place little reliance upon him. The man is a craven. Oh, he's brave enough when he knows he has the upper hand, but when faced with real danger he is a coward and a scoundrel."

"Your Grace sounds as though we were doomed!"

"We must not give up hope," replied Cranmer. "This place is well guarded. Your father and I will remain here with you until . . . until this matter is decided."

"Sirs," she said calmly, only wanting to get away from them, "we are all worn with anxiety. As for me, I am going to bed. Good night."

They did not kneel as she left the room.

The next day the little Queen got out of bed and, seated by the window, was served breakfast by both Mrs. Ashley and Mrs. Ellen. They were distraught and their hands were shaking.

"What is it?" asked Jane.

"Bad news, Your Majesty," said Mrs. Ellen. "Mary was proclaimed queen at Oxford and Norwich. The regent, learning of the number that follow her, has sent to London for more troops. He is now at Cambridge, waiting."

The Queen's eyes flooded with tears and the food had no appeal for her. "It's only a few days since Edward died. He would have made an ideal monarch. I cannot stop grieving for him. During the last few years of his life I discerned a certain bigotry in him, but I know this was fostered by Somerset. He would have outgrown it, for he was the soul of kindness. I dreamed of the day when he would truly rule. Little did I—" She broke off, her voice choked with sobs.

"I know you placed your whole heart upon him," said Mrs. Ellen soothingly. "I know how sincere your sorrow is; even worse than when the Queen Dowager died."

"Yes."

"It is wise to think of the future rather than the past," said Mrs. Ashley. "And a splendid future it will be, with you on the throne."

"It will be over a year before I can really rule," answered Jane, making an effort to stifle her tears, "but I vow to serve the people loyally and fairly. I shall encourage art, learning, literature, and music. I shall see to it that the people may worship each in accord with his conscience."

As news continued to reach London that the nobility of the nearby counties were shifting to Mary's support and that Northumberland's men were defecting, the members of the council—those who only a few days earlier had sworn allegiance to Queen Jane—realized that if they were to save their lives, they must side with Mary, and quickly. With Northumberland in the field and his iron control at a safe distance, the lords quietly left London and gathered at the Earl of Pembroke's country residence. Arundel was the chief speaker, and the nobles were easily persuaded that it was Mary, not Northumberland, who would prevail. It was only a step to declaring that Northumberland was a traitor and that he must surrender and dismiss his army. It was decided that if the council had no word from him, Arundel should go into the field and arrest the man who had caused them to betray their rightful queen.

No message having been received from Northumberland, Arundel left for Cambridge about the nineteenth—first to make his own peace with Mary and to bear her a petition from the council, asking her forgiveness. Word was sent to London that Queen Jane's brief reign was over, and Mary was proclaimed queen in the city and the provinces. The Spanish and French ambassadors, who had received so many conflicting reports during the past two weeks, were told that Mary was officially queen.

Northumberland, outside Cambridge, saw his soldiers deserting by the hundreds. Now, at last, he began to realize that the people constituted power. He recalled that as he had marched through London at the head of his army, the crowds, though Protestant, had shown their hatred of him by sullen silence.

"The people crowd to look at us," he had said then, "but not one cried 'God speed you!' "

When he received the council's message to surrender, he realized that defeat, if not death, was inevitable. He himself, in the market place, tore down the banner proclaiming Queen Jane's accession.

"Long live Queen Mary!" he cried, the tears running down his cheeks. He still hoped to escape capture, together with his sons, and went to his lodgings to prepare for flight. A loud knock at the door revealed Arundel. As Northumberland hesitated, Arundel strode into the room.

"You tried to make yourself master!" Arundel shouted. "Your soldiers have deserted! The fleet has declared in

Queen Mary's favor. The men of every shire have proclaimed that they will fight only in her cause!"

For a moment the once-haughty Northumberland stood looking about in panic at the hostile faces. "Queen Mary is a merciful woman," he cried. "Be good to me," he pleaded to Arundel. "I have done nothing that was not ordained by the council. Have mercy on me!"

"My Lord," Arundel replied coldly, "if you had sought mercy, it should have been sooner. I now arrest you in the name of the Queen."

Northumberland was hustled away.

In London, Jane, Guilford, Henry and Frances Grey, the Duchess of Northumberland, and their attendants were still in the Tower. It was there that Henry received word that Northumberland had been arrested for treason, and he himself tore down the royal canopy in the state apartment. Jane, on learning of Northumberland's defeat and the end of her brief reign, was undismayed. "I put off my royal robes much more willingly than I put them on," she said. And then she added, "May I not go home now?"

Her father, weak in this as in every crisis, knew what he must do at once if he were to save his neck. With scarcely a backward thought for his daughter, he left the Tower and proclaimed his allegiance to Queen Mary. Then he left hastily for Sheen, where he was joined a few days later by Lady Frances. Jane was never to see her parents again. She remained in her private apartments, attended by her heartbroken and weeping ladies; she did not even see Guilford, who was in another part of the Tower.

Northumberland, a prisoner, was led back to London, where he arrived on July 25. When the townspeople saw him in chains, they howled with joy and pelted him with mud and refuse. "Death to the traitor!" they cried. In order to add to his humiliation, his captor Arundel caused him to remove first his hat and then his scarlet cloak, but still the people recognized him, and there was even a chance that he might be lynched by the furious mobs.

But the duke retained his arrogance and bearing and gave no sign that he was a beaten and doomed man. His sons showed no such fortitude, and one of them was seen to drop his reins and burst into tears as he buried his head in his arms.

The Duchess of Northumberland, hearing of her husband's ignominious return, hastened to Queen Mary to plead his cause. Mary was in Beaulieu by this time, having decided to linger there a few days to rest before making a grand entrance into London. The duchess fell on her knees before Mary, pleading wildly on her husband's behalf, but Mary ordered her to be taken away.

Jane, left with only her attendants, was moved from the royal apartments to the prisoners' part of the Tower. She had expected to be put in a dungeon, but instead she was conducted to a room reserved for important prisoners; though small, it was clean and comfortable. She expected no pity; Mary was queen and she was a prisoner.

There was considerable consternation in the Tower that day, for suddenly there was an influx of noble guests—none other than the girl who yesterday had been queen; Northumberland, who had been their master, and his five sons, including Guilford; Henry Grey, who had been arrested at Sheen but was soon to be released again; and several other nobles who had joined Northumberland's ill-fated expedition against Mary.

Queen Mary herself rode into London on August 3. Princess Elizabeth, escorted by a vast retinue of horsemen and ladies, was waiting outside the gates to receive her. The lord mayor and the aldermen proclaimed her queen while the people cheered, church bells rang, and bonfires flamed in the streets. In Mary's train those who had so vehemently vowed to uphold Protestantism now appeared wearing rosaries and heavy crosses, and all of them declared that at heart they had always been stanch Catholics. As she had ridden from Beaulieu, Mary had seen them fall to their knees before her, had heard their cries of devotion and homage and their frenzied pledges to serve her.

She and her cousin Jane were indeed living in a strange, unpredictable world where hypocrisy was rife, loyalty was a word without meaning, and fidelity was equated solely with power.

February 12, 1554

When Mary entered London she went to the royal apartment in the Tower, where she would remain until after Edward's funeral. Scarcely had she arrived when her cousin, Frances Grey, was announced. Dramatically she threw herself at Mary's feet and tearfully swore that she wanted to become a Catholic. Mary nodded coldly but did not order her to rise.

"Your Majesty," wailed Lady Frances, "let me plead for my husband! I beg you to release him. He, too, wishes to become a Catholic. He is your faithful and humble servant. He is very ill and if he is kept in the Tower he will die! I beseech you, Madame, let him go. Let him prove his loyalty!"

Not once did she mention Jane, and neither did Mary. The Queen listened as the duchess continued to protest that she and her husband were Mary's devoted servants and that in the future nothing, nothing in all the world would swerve them from their allegiance to their rightful sovereign. The painful scene ended when Mary called for quill and paper, signed Henry Grey's pardon—which required him to pay a fine of £20,000—and handed the document to Lady Frances.

She had already signed Northumberland's death warrant. His execution was to take place in less than six weeks. Her advisers kept insisting that she show no mercy to Jane. Jane, they affirmed, would always be a threat to Mary's crown; but Mary, knowing Jane so well, could feel only sympathy for her.

"Treat her kindly," the Queen ordered.

In her bleak, unadorned room containing only a bed, a table, and several chairs, Jane was attended by Mrs. Ellen and Mrs. Ashley as well as by two strange serving maids who cleaned the room, took care of her laundry, and served her meals, which, though plain, were adequate.

In another part of the Tower were Guilford and his brothers as well as Archbishop Cranmer. Jane was not permitted to see any of them.

The day after her arrest she was visited by Stephen Gardiner, Catherine's old enemy, who was now Queen Mary's chief minister. His attitude was hostile.

"My Lady," he began, "in inspecting the crown jewels preparatory to the coronation of our gracious Queen, I find that several are missing. I demand their return."

"Are you accusing me of stealing them, My Lord?"

"I find them missing, My Lady. Therefore I am come to inform you that all your personal jewels are hereby confiscated, as well as whatever money and property you and your husband may have."

She knew it was no use trying to prevent this or even protesting her innocence. The charge was false, in keeping with the character of Stephen Gardiner, who now left the room considerably the richer.

This was Jane's only contact with the outside world until several days later when Gardiner again entered her room, carrying an official document.

"This has previously been read to your husband, My Lady. It is the Queen's indictment against you."

Jane listened quietly as he read it. In legal verbiage it declared that the Lady Jane Grey, Guilford Dudley, and Thomas Cranmer were accused of treason. When he had finished reading, he turned and left the room hurriedly.

The prisoner asked for writing implements and when these had been brought she began writing Mary a lengthy letter, a "witness of my innocence and the disburdening of my conscience," as she wrote. She did not mention their relationship or their former close association. In a straightforward, dignified way, without pleas or dramatics, she simply told what had happened from the day of her betrothal to the day of her arrest. Mentioning Mary's "infinite clemency," Jane referred to her "error" in taking the crown as not "altogether caused by myself. For whereas I might take upon me that of which I was not worthy, yet no one can ever say either that I sought it or that I was pleased with it."

Reading the letter, Mary knew that it contained only the truth. The last time she had seen Jane was at Beaulieu in the summer of 1552—about a year earlier, but she knew that Jane had not changed. The girl was innocent of intrigue and had been merely a pawn in the hands of Northumberland; but Mary did not reply to the letter. The very fact that Jane existed was troublesome. On all sides her advisers were still urging her to do away with her cousin.

"Unless Jane Grey is beheaded," they insisted, "Your Majesty will never be safe."

She heard them in silence, but she could not bring herself to sign the death warrant.

One of Mary's first acts was to see to the burial of her half brother Edward. In spite of the admonitions of Arundel, who had taken over Northumberland's position in the council, Mary insisted that the burial take place in Westminster Abbey with Protestant rites; she herself would attend a requiem Mass for him.

When Northumberland and his closest conspirators were brought to trial on August 18 they pleaded guilty. Upon entering the Tower Northumberland had collapsed, and now his tall body shook convulsively as he heard that he would be put to death on the twenty-third. Questioned about Jane, he answered honestly that she "had only accepted the crown through enticement and force."

Following this trial, which was not really a trial at all,

Mary was again strongly advised to show no mercy to Jane. Still the Queen did nothing. Yet she bowed to the Spanish ambassador's entreaties to the extent of leaving Jane and Guilford in prison for the time being.

"I cannot find it in my heart or conscience to put my unfortunate kinswoman to death," she said. "She has not been an accomplice of Northumberland, but merely an instrument in his hands. If there was any crime in being his daughter-in-law, my cousin Jane is not guilty even of that, for she was legally contracted to the Earl of Hertford and therefore her marriage to Lord Guilford Dudley was not valid. As for any danger existing from her pretension to the throne, it is only imaginary, and every requisite precaution shall be taken before she is set at liberty. Now let us hear no more about this."

Set at liberty! It could only mean that eventually she intended to free Lady Jane.

In her cell, the object of this discussion had found a singular peace. The late summer was intensely hot, with many storms, and on dry days she was permitted to stroll in the garden. From this vantage point she could see the numerous preparations being made for Mary's coronation.

Hearing the tolling of a bell on the morning of the twenty-third, she asked one of her maids who was to be beheaded.

"It is that monster, Northumberland. They permitted him to bid farewell to Lord Guilford, and he is now being taken to Tower Hill. He turned at the end to the Catholic faith, but if he thought to stay the executioner by this act, he was mistaken."

"Would you be so kind as to request the governor of the Tower to permit me to see my husband for a few minutes? Perhaps I may be able to give him a few words of comfort."

"I will ask, My Lady."

After several hours the guard came to tell her that she

would be permitted to spend ten minutes with her husband. She found him in a room smaller than her own. Without interest, showing neither joy nor surprise, he looked up at her.

"I came to comfort you," she explained.

"How can you comfort me?" he replied coldly.

"For the death of your father. I know how much he loved you."

"He deserved death," replied Guilford bitterly. "Had it not been for him, you and I would not be here. Will they execute us, too?"

"I don't know. I have written to the Queen explaining everything. I don't expect her to reply. I only wanted her to understand how it happened."

"What did you say? Did you plead for me? Tell me what you said!"

"I said I was willing to admit my fault, if such fault may be absolved by a full confession. I described my consternation and confusion when my father and mother, as well as my father-in-law and mother-in-law, announced to me the death of Edward, at the same time doing me homage as queen."

"Well?"

"I told how they informed me that by virtue of Edward's will I was left heiress to the throne. I told her how I fell to the ground and swooned, overcome with grief at the tiding, which I truly felt to be disastrous to me. I declared that when I was brought to the Tower as queen the crown was brought to me by the Bishop of Winchester to try it on my head to see how it would fit, and he brought it of his own accord, unsent for by me or by anyone in my name, and how he said he would have another made for you. I told her how I objected to this and how you all treated me, especially you and your mother."

"Do you know when we'll be brought to trial?"

"No. I am told very little. But they are not unkind. At least they haven't put us to the torture."

"I hear the Queen is to be crowned on the first of October."

"Long may she live!"

"She is your mother's cousin. She might pardon us. I hear she has pardoned your father. But if you and I were freed, do you realize we'd not have a ha'penny? Gardiner informed me that some of the crown jewels are missing, and for this he holds you responsible. He said that all the money, jewels, and property belonging to you and me would be confiscated. That means we are paupers."

"I know; but this doesn't seem to matter, since I doubt that we'll ever be free."

"You mean we'll be kept here forever?"

"I am prepared for anything," she replied quietly.

"Even death on the block?"

"Even that. Well, I came to comfort you, thinking to find you grief-stricken. I was allowed only ten minutes. I must go now. I suppose we shall be tried together. I shall not see you until then. God be with you, Guilford."

His mouth quivered like that of a small boy on the verge of tears. Not wishing her to see this, he turned away and stood gazing out of the window until he heard the door close softly behind her.

September passed uneventfully. Jane made no complaints and requested no extra service, except to ask for a Bible. This was promptly brought, and most of her time was spent reading it. Her few attendants and her guards came to love her, for she gave them no trouble.

"She is an angel," was the general opinion. "She is an angel—and she looks like an angel."

On October 1 she could hear the shouts of the people, the cannon booming and the church bells ringing as Mary Tudor was crowned Queen of England. If Jane's attendants expected her to betray any jealousy, envy, or bitterness on that occasion they were disappointed.

Mary, unhealthy-looking and homely, seemed old and drab beside her younger sister. Elizabeth, dressed to perfection in pale blue velvet, was vivid and animated. And there was Anne of Cleves, Henry's divorced wife, glittering with jewels, as well as Jane's parents, the Duke and Duchess of Suffolk, smiling broadly.

Though still unpopular, Mary was given this enthusiastic greeting because the people rejoiced that justice had been done. Rigidly disciplined, she showed no emotion whatsoever.

Elizabeth had now become heiress presumptive to the crown. Wisely, she had taken no part in the struggle between Mary's and Northumberland's factions, and she was utterly indifferent to the fate of the girl who was a prisoner in the Tower.

Almost a month and a half after Mary's coronation, on November 13, Jane, Guilford, and Archbishop Cranmer were arraigned at Guildhall, where they were to be given a court trial. They left the Tower on foot in the morning. Jane was attended by her four women, who walked behind her. Ahead of her was Cranmer, between two special guards, and in the rear came Guilford, plainly attired in a black suit.

The prisoners were escorted by four hundred halberdiers. At the very front of the procession walked a tall man carrying an ax. In going toward the place of the trial, the ax was turned away from the culprits, as was the custom. Now the people saw Jane, not as a queen who had ben foisted upon them by a man they hated, but as a delicate, flower-like girl, both she and her women dressed in black and wearing long black capes. Among the crowd there were whispers.

"Oh, but she's lovely!"

"I didn't realize she was just a child!"

"She's such a *little* lady!"

At Guildhall many nobles were assembled. Knowing her youth, they expected to be subjected to tears and panic, but Jane was dignified and composed. An attendant led her to a chair with a footstool. Her four women grouped behind her. Cranmer and Guilford were placed some distance away, each in a separate pew. The trial was brief.

When the indictment had been read aloud, a voice called, "Lady Jane Grey, how do you plead?"

"Guilty," answered Jane in a soft, calm voice.

The court clerk then turned to the two men. "Sirs, how do you plead?"

"Guilty," they chorused.

That was all. There were no witnesses, no cross-examinations, no arguments for the defense. The jury, citizens of Middlesex, now withdrew to a private room. Here, without hesitation, they decided unanimously that Guilford and the archbishop must die on the block. But Jane? There were many arguments. Some maintained that she should die as a traitor. Others insisted that she was harmless, a mere child, simply a tool in the hands of Northumberland.

When at last they filed back into the courtroom and took their seats, the Lord Chief Justice, Sir Richard Morgan, rose and read from a paper that Lord Guilford Dudley and Thomas Cranmer were sentenced to being hanged, drawn and quartered. Jane Grey was to be "burnt alive or beheaded as the Queen shall please."

There was no sound from the condemned. They left the room in the same order as they had arrived, only now the man who carried the ax had reversed its position: The blade pointed toward the prisoners, a sign indicating that they had been condemned. A crowd had gathered; seeing the position of the ax, and gazing upon Jane's sweet young face, many women wept. Hundreds followed the prisoners as they returned to the Tower jail.

"Surely the Queen will pardon her!" some of them said.

"She's so young. I saw her at her coronation. Odd, how much smaller she looks now."

"So beautiful! Surely she wasn't to blame."

"Ah, the poor thing. The poor little thing! There's only goodness in that face."

Jane did not hear these comments. She was silently praying, and these prayers sustained her.

Arriving at the Tower, while the guard dispersed, she had only a moment to talk to her two companions. "Remember, My Lords," she said in an effort to comfort them, "death is not an end. It is but a beginning to a new and nobler life. We must not fear it. Our God is good, our God is love, and He will never forsake us."

They did not answer.

No date had been set for their execution, and the men, though filled with despair, told themselves that they might still hope for a pardon.

Returning to Jane's quiet room, Mrs. Ellen and Mrs. Ashley and the two serving women who had grown to know the girl so well burst into tears. She soothed them by quoting various inspiring passages from the Bible.

"To see you die—like that!" wailed Mrs. Ellen.

"Come, my dear," Jane answered composedly. "Edward is dead. Catherine is dead. And yet I know that they have not ceased to be. Only to our blindness have they seemed to die; yet God is their Father and He knows them as His children, blessed and safe and happy. I am resigned to what is called death."

"If only I had faith like that!" sobbed Mrs. Ashley.

"Think! What has my life been in these seventeen years? Subjected to torment by my parents and finally forced to do what I never wanted to do. Gladly do I exchange such an existence for one that I believe is a better one."

So she talked and they were comforted.

"I have known that girl all her life," said Mrs. Ashley after

Jane had bade them good night. "I have never known her to say or do an unkind thing. Surely, if ever there was an angel on earth, it is the Lady Jane Grey. Let us thank God that she has been given such a sustaining and unwavering faith."

When the weather was sufficiently mild, Jane still took her short, lonely walk in the Tower garden, and those who watched were amazed that there was no change in her. She was at peace within herself. Her faith in the high teachings and promises of the New Testament supplied her with a certain armor. She could smile her soft, friendly smile at the men who guarded her.

If there was no change in Jane's surroundings, there was much of it in the world outside. The people's enthusiasm for Mary, which was actually their joy at being rid of Northumberland, had waned. She whom history was to record as "Bloody Mary" now began to move swiftly to re-establish Catholicism.

Married priests were driven from their churches. The images were replaced. Mass was restored. As yet she had not dared refuse the title of "head of the Church," but she was determined ultimately to restore that authority to the Pope.

In the years since Henry had presumptuously proclaimed himself head of the Church, the majority of the people had accepted the teachings of Protestantism. Now forced to worship in a way that was strange to them, they looked on disapprovingly. The excitement of Mary's fight for the throne had subsided, and many began to suspect that they had been mistaken in championing her cause. The nation was restive.

The nobles of the court, however, most of whom were insincere and concerned only with self-aggrandizement, pretended to be gladdened by what the Queen was doing. They brought out rosaries and flaunted them before the sick-looking, white-faced Queen. Among these sycophants were the Duke and Duchess of Suffolk, who, ostentatious in their services to the Queen, never mentioned the fact that their daughter was facing death in the Tower.

But the duke had many moments when he remembered the past—the brief time Jane had worn the crown, his arrest and pardon; and his mind went even farther back—to the time when King Henry had sent him to tell Anne of Cleves that he meant to divorce her, or when Henry had commissioned him to force a confession from his fifth wife, poor Catherine Howard. Yes, he had led an eventful life. He was now in his mid-forties, suave, polished, apparently carefree, but he must watch every word he said, and so long as Queen Mary remained in power he must please and compliment her.

His wife was in high favor with the Queen, but despite his fervent protestations of loyalty, it was clear that Mary did not quite trust him. She ignored him, and because of this royal disfavor he was snubbed by many who had once been proud to entertain him. This secretly irked him.

When Mary's intentions of marrying Philip of Spain became known, the reaction of the people was so pronounced that Henry Grey began to suspect that Mary might not be in power long. If this feeling continued, he mused, it might be possible to get rid of her; and Jane, after all, might become queen!

The people dreaded this Spanish marriage, fearing that it would re-establish the supremacy of the Pope. One frequently heard statements of pity for the poor little prisoner in the Tower, who, it was said, was bearing her ordeal so bravely. Shrewdly, Henry Grey estimated the general mood. For the present he must do nothing, since Mary, bowing to the will of her subjects, might be forced to repudiate her promise to Philip. On the other hand, since she possessed the Tudor stubbornness, she might not.

While he pretended approval of the marriage, his scheming

mind foresaw a triumph for himself. No, he was not beaten! Ambition began to surge in him again. He had seen many changes. If Mary persisted in going ahead with this marriage, she was certainly in for trouble. He might yet be exalted as the father of the queen!

In her cell, ignored by her family, Jane waited patiently for death. Every time the door opened she expected that the stern-faced governor of the Tower had come to inform her coldly that she must prepare to face the executioner.

Even freedom held no promise for her. What would it consist of but being the wife of Guilford? When Mrs. Ashley told her that the Queen, against the wishes of her subjects, was planning to marry Philip of Spain, Jane said only that she wished them happiness. The marriage, she thought, had nothing to do with her.

Mary had sent a priest, Father Feckenham, to the Tower to convert her. A kindly, gentle man, he arrived each day to converse with her on theological subjects, pleading with her to save her soul before it was too late.

While these discussions were going on, her father was having secret discussions with his two brothers, Lord Thomas and Lord John Grey. At first they were reluctant to have anything to do with his scheme.

"I tell you," he insisted vehemently, "the country is seething over this marriage with Spain! The people are unhappy under Mary and ready to rise against her. All they need is leadership. Somerset and Northumberland are dead. We can easily gain control now! And Jane still lives!"

"As far as I know," said Lord Thomas, "no one is honestly for this marriage. You are right about that, Henry. The Queen refuses to consider the feelings of her people. If the marriage takes place, England will be a mere province under the rule of Spain. But Her Majesty continues with her preparations to receive her bridegroom. Meanwhile, I heard it rumored that Elizabeth is conspiring with Sir Thomas Wyatt to topple her sister through some form of insurrection. Of course, it may not be true."

"Or it may be!" cried Henry. "All the more reason for us to strike as soon as possible!"

"Strike?" asked John. "How? Where?"

"Leicestershire is my own land. Jane was born there. There we each have estates and hundreds of tenants. There we could raise a force quickly. Between us we have the money to do it. The people believe that England will be transferred to Philip as Mary's dowry. We can stress that. We can make them believe it!"

"I think you go too fast," said John. "This is a risky business. We'll pay with our heads for failure."

"But think what we have to gain if we win! I tell you, the people will join us. In a few weeks we could raise a force that would—"

"Does your wife know of this?" asked Thomas.

"No. She's content at court. I see her rarely these days. I tell you, we must work fast! Just yesterday the ambassador from Spain concluded the marriage treaty. We must take advantage of the storm that is surely brewing. Why, as he passed through Kent the man was almost torn to pieces!"

Between them the three brothers finally reached an agreement and a plan.

The marriage treaty between Queen Mary and Philip II was signed on January 12, 1554, and the people of England learned shortly thereafter that the betrothal was official.

So swiftly did the Grey brothers work that within two weeks after the engagement became a certainty, they had amassed their force of brawny Leicester men, patriots all, who were determined to rescue their country from the threat of domination by Spain. The general uprising was set for January 25.

Mary was momentarily stunned by the news that simultaneously there were several uprisings against her in various districts. In the mid-counties the vassals of Henry Grey were stoutly avowing their intention to depose Mary and restore the crown to Lady Jane. In the west of England Sir Peter Carew fought with his forces to establish the Protestant religion and place Princess Elizabeth on the throne. The third and largest force, headed by young Sir Thomas Wyatt, was mustered in Kent, southeast of London.

Thomas Wyatt, the son of a noted English poet and diplomat, was Catholic, but he had come to detest the Spaniards and was determined to prevent Mary's marriage to Philip. Wyatt was convinced that his rebellion would succeed. Though he did not intend to renounce either his queen or his religion, he hoped to force Mary to abandon the projected marriage by threatening to displace her by either Princess Elizabeth or Jane.

When Mary received news of Wyatt's uprising, she summoned Henry Grey to Windsor to head her forces. It was not until then that she learned that he had raised a band of rebels in Leicestershire and was proclaiming Jane queen in every town.

In an emergency Mary was superb. She sent part of her army, headed by Sir William Herbert, the Earl of Pembroke, to suppress the uprising headed by Henry Grey. The two forces clashed near Coventry; after a fierce battle the Grey brothers, seeing that they could not win, ran off but were captured. Carew's attempt met with equal disaster, but he had been more cautious and was able to escape to France, by boat. It took somewhat longer to subdue the larger army headed by Wyatt.

When the battles ended, Mary, perfectly calm, rode out to see the horror of war—dead bodies, men screaming with pain, and blood everywhere. Standing amid the havoc, she heard someone say, "This will happen again and again as long as Lady Jane Grey lives!"

She knew it was true.

On February 6, 1554, when Henry Grey and his brothers were brought prisoners to the Tower, Mary signed Jane's death warrant: "To be beheaded on Tower Hill on February 9, Lord Guilford Dudley and his wife."

Later that day the news was brought to Jane.

"As the Queen wishes," she said. "I am ready."

There were no tears. Her meekness and tranquillity amazed the governor of the Tower.

"There is always the possibility of a reprieve," he informed her.

"My life has been a living torment, and the sooner it is ended, the better. I am ready to receive death patiently in whatever manner it may please the Queen to appoint. True, my flesh shudders, as is natural to frail humanity, at what I have to go through, but I fervently hope the spirit will spring with rejoicing into the presence of the eternal God who will receive it. I would, if I could, plead for my husband. He is innocent. He only obeyed his father in all things."

"Has Your Ladyship any requests?"

"Only that I may receive a minister of my own religion."

"The Queen has forbidden that. Only Father Feckenham will be permitted, but the Queen graciously permits an interview with your husband if this will in any way comfort you."

Jane considered this for a moment and then shook her head. Such a meeting might cause a display of emotion that would only weaken them both.

"It is better that we do not meet. It would be too disturbing."

Several hours after the governor left, Father Feckenham entered—a short, stout man who had grown to respect Jane and who expected to find her in abject sorrow. Gently and lovingly he told her that he had seen the Queen and prevailed upon her to postpone the executions until February 12.

"Alas, sir," said the prisoner, "I would not have you think me covetous for a moment's longer life, for I am solicitous for a better life in eternity, and will gladly suffer death, since it is Her Majesty's pleasure."

Guilford took the news differently. He broke into violent tears.

"Your wife," he was told, "being of royal blood, is to be executed inside the Tower, but you, not being of the blood royal, are to die outside the Tower."

"May I see Jane before—"

"She feels that this would be too disturbing for both of you."

Sunday, the day before she was to die, Jane wrote a letter to her sister Catherine and one to her father. Next morning at ten o'clock she was standing at her window when she saw the tall, handsome figure of her husband, dressed in black velvet, walking to his doom. He chanced to glance up and their eyes met. He was not weeping now. They waved to each other and then she lost sight of him.

Only a few minutes later—so speedily was it over—she saw his body being carried back in a cart. Now for the first time her composure deserted her. She put her hands over her face and wept. "Oh, Guilford, Guilford," she was heard to say.

Then Father Feckenham told her pityingly that the procession was forming to conduct her to the scaffold. She dried her eyes and nodded. At eleven the drums began to beat, low and insistent. It was a quiet, misty morning.

The procession moved slowly. At its head were two hundred yeomen, followed by the tall, powerfully built executioner, dressed in red, his face masked. At his side came his assistant, who carried the sharp, gleaming ax. Next came two sheriffs, the Tower officials, and the constable.

Following them was a slight, girlish figure in black with a black velvet cap sufficiently back on her head to reveal light brown hair, parted in the middle, waving slightly and brushed neatly over her ears. Suspended from the cap in the back was a long veil reaching to a slim waist. Her long, closely fitted sleeves were edged at the wrists by narrow pleated ruffles of white lawn.

Again everyone was aware of her tinyness and her youth, her fresh, petal-like skin, her singular beauty and exquisite poise. Beside her, gravely holding his Bible, walked Father Feckenham. Behind her, weeping copiously, were the faithful Mrs. Ellen, Mrs. Ashley, and the two women who had served her since her arrest six months before. About five hundred people had gathered to witness the tragic spectacle, but Jane seemed not to know they were there. As she walked she read from a prayer book.

The scaffold had been strewn with fresh straw. Before ascending the four steps leading up to it, Jane turned to embrace the weeping women. The people cried out plaintively in a long, shrill moan.

"No! No!"

"Illustrious Lady," asked Father Feckenham in a low, compassionate voice, "what shall I read to you?"

"Psalm fifty-one," she answered.

" 'Have mercy upon me, O God, according to thy loving kindness: according unto the multitude of thy tender mercies blot out my transgressions. . . . Restore unto me the joy of thy salvation; and uphold me with thy free spirit. . . .' "

Epilogue

This brief postscript will give some indication of what befell the people whom we have been following.

Henry Grey followed his daughter to the scaffold about ten days later.

Lady Frances, his wife, having lost her daughter, husband, son-in-law, and brother-in-law within a few weeks, spent no time in repining. Two weeks after Henry Grey's death she married his groom of chambers, a man some fifteen years younger than she. Strangely, throughout Queen Mary's reign Lady Frances was a favorite at court; she took precedence over all other peeresses and sometimes even over Princess Elizabeth. In the five years left to her, she bore her new husband two sons.

Thomas Grey, Henry's brother, was beheaded in April, 1554, for his part in the rebellion against Queen Mary.

John Grey, the other brother, was released after two trials.

Catherine Grey, Jane's younger sister, married in name only to the Earl of Pembroke's son, was recognized as a liability after the greater part of her family had been executed, and the marriage was quickly dissolved. A few years later she married clandestinely the Earl of Hertford—that same young man whose name had been linked with her sister Jane's. Elizabeth, who was queen at the time, was so infuriated by not being told of the marriage that she sent the young couple to the Tower: the earl for "venturing to marry an heiress to the throne." Catherine remained a prisoner for the rest of her life, either in the Tower or under house arrest, but managed nonetheless to bear her husband three sons. These, as potential threat to Queen Elizabeth as heirs to the throne, were declared illegitimate until after the Queen's death.

Mary Grey, Jane's youngest sister, also incurred Queen Elizabeth's displeasure when, in 1565, she secretly married Martin Keyes, the Queen's sergeant-porter, a giant of a man. Mary, it will be recalled, was practically a dwarf. (Apparently the betrothal referred to in the book had collapsed.) Both Lady Mary and her husband were kept in custody until after his death, at which time Lady Mary was released.

The Duchess of Northumberland died, heartbroken, in 1555.

John Dudley, Duke of Warwick, her eldest son, was sentenced to death at the same time as his father, but was pardoned. However, he died ten days after his release from the Tower.

Ambrose Dudley, a younger son, was pardoned and released in 1554.

Robert Dudley, another son, also condemned to death by Queen Mary in 1554, was pardoned the same year. Later, as the Earl of Leicester, he became a great favorite of Queen Elizabeth. His wife Amy broke her neck in a fall, perhaps engineered to dispose of her so that Leicester could marry Elizabeth, but the marriage never took place. In 1578 Leicester remarried.

Queen Mary I, perhaps better known to history as "Bloody Mary," did marry Philip II of Spain in the summer of 1554. She re-established Catholicism in England and persecuted the Protestants. She had no children; thus, after her brief five-year reign, the crown passed at her death to her half sister Elizabeth—in accordance with Henry VIII's will.

Elizabeth I was imprisoned in March, 1554, following Wyatt's rebellion, but there was no proof of her complicity in the uprising and after two months her imprisonment was gradually relaxed. She was able to return to Hatfield by autumn, 1555. She succeeded Mary to the throne in 1558. Her persecution of the young Mary, Queen of Scots, in the late 1560's incurred the wrath of the Catholic princes, among them Philip II of Spain, and was one of the precipitating causes of the Spanish Armada. Elizabeth's reign is too well known to discuss here.

Mary, Queen of Scots, the mother of James VI of Scotland, was beheaded by Queen Elizabeth. Nonetheless, after Elizabeth's death her son became King of England as James I, the first Stuart ruler. It was during his reign that the King James version of the Bible was prepared.

Archbishop Cranmer was not executed immediately. He was excommunicated and condemned for heresy. He recanted, admitting papal supremacy, but at the last—just before being burned at the stake in 1556—he again did an about-face and upheld the English reformed church.

Thomas Wyatt's trial began the middle of March, 1554, but he was not sent to the block until April—after he had confessed and implicated many noblemen and officials in the plot to prevent Queen Mary from reigning.

A Note about Names

It is often very confusing, when reading English history, to have a person referred to under several names or titles. This is especially true in the earlier periods, when peerages were being made or unmade much more frequently than they are now.

A peer is a nobleman. The ranks of the nobility in descending order are: duke, marquess, earl, viscount, and baron. The system of peerages was gradually developed following the Norman Conquest and involved both exclusive hereditary ranks, with special titles, and landholdings. Gradually, however, the association between title and land has been lost.

A peer holding large estates, as was common during the Tudor era, might then have several titles (plus the wealth that went with them), gained through inheritance or the whim of a monarch. Especially in Henry VIII's reign, when vast Church lands were confiscated, the rewards of being in royal favor could be tremendous.

All peers have family names as well as titles, and the family names are used by the sons and daughters, except in the cases of the eldest sons of dukes, marquesses, and earls. In these ranks the head of the family usually has lesser titles as well, and the eldest son, from the time of his birth, takes the highest of these as his "courtesy title." Upon the death of the father, the son inherits the father's titles as his hereditary *right*.

Thus John Dudley (family name) inherited the title Viscount Lisle in 1542 and was created Earl of Warwick in 1547 and Duke of Northumberland in 1551. He is known to history usually by his highest-ranking title—in this case Northumberland—but between 1547 and 1551 he was called Warwick; and the confusion is increased by having his eldest son, also named John Dudley, bear the title of Warwick from 1551 to the time of his death in 1554; later, in 1561, the title was given to the next younger son, Ambrose. But basically the whole family still remained Dudleys, and in reference works one will sometimes find them discussed under "Dudley" and sometimes under the various titles: Lisle, Warwick, Northumberland, Leicester (a title given to one son, Robert, by Queen Elizabeth I, with whom he is strongly linked in fact and fiction).

Just as a title could be conferred for some special reason, so it could be taken away. Following an act of treason, for example, the person could become *attainted*, which involved not only forfeiture of his property but "corruption of blood," so that he could neither inherit nor pass on his titles. The peerage would then lapse for a shorter or longer period, perhaps to be revived later by some other monarch and given to some quite different family. During the bloody Tudor era, when executions were almost a matter of routine, this happened frequently. Thus the title of Duke of Somerset (Edward Seymour) lapsed when he was beheaded; and the title of Earl of Warwick was in abeyance for several years, until the attainder against the younger John Dudley was removed posthumously.

A list is given below of some of the more important persons appearing in this book, to enable the reader to identify them more easily. They are arranged by family name rather than by title. Within the family, they are listed by seniority rather than alphabetically.

Anne Boleyn, *see* Boleyn.

Anne of Cleves (1515-57); m. (in 1540) Henry VIII, his fourth wife; divorced.

Arundel, Earl of (Henry Fitzalan) (1511?-80), one of the leaders of the Catholic nobility; m. Catherine Grey, sister of Henry Grey.

Ascham, Roger (1515-68), tutor of the young Tudors; later, secretary of Queen Elizabeth.

Aylmer, John (1521-94), tutor of Lady Jane Grey.

Boleyn, Anne (1507-36); m. (in 1533) Henry VIII, his second wife; mother (in 1533) of Elizabeth I; beheaded.

Brandon, Charles (1484?-1545); created Duke of Suffolk (1514); second husband of Mary of France (née Tudor, Henry VIII's younger sister); father of Lady Frances and grandfather of Lady Jane Grey.

Frances, Lady, his daughter, *see* Frances.

Catherine Howard, *see* Howard.

Catherine of Aragon (1485-1536), daughter of Ferdinand and Isabella of Spain; m. (1, from 1501-1502) Arthur, elder brother of Henry VIII; (2, in 1509) Henry VIII, his first wife; mother (in 1516) of Mary Tudor (Mary I); divorced (1533).

Cecil, William (1520-98), secretary of state during Edward VI's reign; active in the service of both Queen Mary and Queen Elizabeth.

Cheke, John (1514-57), tutor to Prince Edward; secretary of state for Jane Grey; imprisoned (1553-54) by Queen Mary, but released.

Cranmer, Thomas (1489-1556), Archbishop of Canterbury (1533); burned at the stake by Queen Mary.

Dorset, Marquess of, *see* Grey, Henry.

Dudley, John (1502-53); created Viscount Lisle (1542); lord high admiral (1543); created Earl of Warwick (1547) and Duke of Northumberland (1551) by Edward VI; executed by Queen Mary.

John, Viscount Lisle (d. 1554), his son; m. (in 1550) Anne Seymour, daughter of Edward Seymour; Earl of Warwick (1551); sentenced to death with his father in 1553, released in 1554, but died ten days later.

Ambrose (1528?-90), another son; created Earl of Warwick (1561).

Robert (1532?-88), another son; m. (in 1549) Amy Robsart; condemned but pardoned by Queen Mary in 1554; later a favorite of Queen Elizabeth; created Earl of Leicester (1564).

Guilford (1533?-54), another son; m. (in 1553) Lady Jane Grey; beheaded by Queen Mary.

Catherine, a daughter; m. (in 1553) Henry Hastings, son
of the Earl of Huntington.
Mary, a daughter; m. Henry Sidney.

Edward VI (1537-53), son of Henry VIII and Jane Seymour;
became king in 1547.
Elizabeth I (1533-1603), daughter of Henry VIII and Anne
Boleyn; became queen in 1558.

Frances, Lady (1517-59), daughter of Charles Brandon and
Mary of France (née Tudor); niece of Henry VIII; m. (1, in
1534) Henry Grey; mother of Jane, Catherine, and Mary
Grey; m. (2, in 1554) Adrian Stokes.

Gardiner, Stephen (1483?-1555); Bishop of Winchester (1531);
imprisoned during the reign of Edward VI but reinstated
and made lord chancellor by Queen Mary (1553).
Grey, Henry (1510-54); created Marquess of Dorset (1530); m.
(in 1534) Lady Frances Brandon; created Duke of Suffolk
(1551); beheaded by Queen Mary.
Jane (1537-54), his daughter, grandniece of Henry VIII; m.
(in 1553) Guilford Dudley; queen July 10-19, 1553; be-
headed by Queen Mary.
Catherine (1538?-67), his second daughter; m. (1, in 1553)
Henry Herbert; divorced; (2, in 1561) Edward Seymour,
Earl of Hertford; imprisoned for many years for having
incurred Queen Elizabeth's displeasure, and died in prison.
Mary (1540?-78), his third daughter; m. (in 1565) Martin
Keyes, sergeant-porter of Queen Elizabeth.
Grey, John (d. 1569), brother of Henry Grey; captured with his
brother but released by Queen Mary after two trials.
Grey, Thomas (d. 1554), brother of Henry Grey; beheaded by
Queen Mary.

Hastings, George (1488-1544); created Earl of Huntington
(1529).
Francis (1514?-60), his oldest son; created Earl of Huntington
(1544); ally of John Dudley, with whom he was captured
(in 1553); later in favor with Queen Mary.
Henry (1535-95), son of Francis; m. (in 1553) Catherine
Dudley, daughter of the Duke of Northumberland;
created Earl of Huntington (1560).

Edward (1520?-72), second son of George; lord chamberlain under Queen Mary.

Henry VIII (1491-1547), son of Henry VII; became king in 1509; m. (1, in 1509) Catherine of Aragon, widow of his brother Arthur; (2, in 1533) Anne Boleyn; (3, in 1536) Jane Seymour; (4, in 1540) Anne of Cleves; (5, in 1540) Catherine Howard; (6, in 1543) Catherine Parr. Father of Mary I (b. 1516); Elizabeth I (b. 1533); Edward VI (b. 1537).

Herbert, William (1501?-70); m. (in 1543) Anne Parr, sister of Catherine Parr; created Earl of Pembroke (1551).

Henry (1534?-1601), his son; m. (in 1553) Catherine Grey, sister of Lady Jane Grey; divorced; created Earl of Pembroke (1570).

Hertford, Earl of, *see* Seymour, Edward.

Howard, Catherine (1520?-42); m. (in 1540) Henry VIII, his fifth wife; beheaded.

Howard, Thomas (1473-1554), Duke of Norfolk; uncle of two of Henry VIII's wives, Anne Boleyn and Catherine Howard, both beheaded; godfather of Edward VI.

Huntington, Earl of, *see* Hastings family.

James IV of Scotland (1473-1513); m. (in 1503) Margaret Tudor, elder sister of Henry VIII; father of James V.

James V of Scotland (1512-42), son of James IV and nephew of Henry VIII; m. (in 1538) Mary of Guise; father (in 1542) of Mary, Queen of Scots (Mary Stuart).

Latimer, Lady, *see* Parr, Catherine.

Leicester, Earl of, *see* Dudley, Robert.

Louis XII, King of France (1462-1515); m. (in 1514) Mary, younger sister of Henry VIII.

Margaret Tudor (1489-1541), elder sister of Henry VIII; m. (in 1503) James IV of Scotland; mother (in 1512) and regent of James V.

Mary, Queen of Scots (Mary Stuart) (1542-87), daughter of James V of Scotland; m. (1, in 1558) Francis II of France; (2, in 1565) Lord Darnley; mother (in 1566) of James VI of Scotland, later James I of England; beheaded by Queen Elizabeth.

Mary of France (née Mary Tudor) (1496-1533), younger sister of Henry VIII; m. (1, in 1514) Louis XII of France; (2, in 1515) Charles Brandon; mother (in 1517) of Lady Frances Brandon.

Mary of Guise (1515-60); m. (in 1538) James V of Scotland; mother (in 1542) of Mary, Queen of Scots.

Mary Tudor (Mary I, "Bloody Mary") (1516-58), daughter of Henry VIII and Catherine of Aragon; became queen in 1553; m. (in 1554) Philip II of Spain.

Norfolk, Duke of, *see* Howard, Thomas.
Northumberland, Duke of, *see* Dudley, John.

Paget, William (1505-63), one of Henry VIII's chief advisers; privy councilor and secretary of state (1543); lord privy seal under Queen Mary (1556-58).

Parr, Anne, sister of Catherine Parr; m. (in 1543) William Herbert.

Parr, Catherine (1512-48); m. (1) Lord Borough; (2) Lord Latimer; (3, in 1543) Henry VIII, his sixth and last wife; (4, in 1547) Thomas Seymour; died following the birth of a daughter.

Pembroke, Earl of, *see* Herbert family.

Philip II of Spain (1527-98); m. (in 1554) Queen Mary (his second wife); became King of Spain in 1556; inherited and conquered vast domains in the Old and New Worlds; developed the Inquisition; lost naval supremacy to England with the defeat of the Armada (1588).

Protector (of Edward VI): Edward Seymour (1547-49); Northumberland succeeded as regent but was not called "Protector."

Seymour, Edward (1506?-52), brother of Jane Seymour; m. Anne Stanhope; created Earl of Hertford (1537); created Duke of Somerset and lord treasurer (1547); Protector of Edward VI (1547-49); beheaded on a charge of felony.

Anne, his daughter; m. (in 1550) John, Viscount Lisle, eldest son of John Dudley.

Edward (1540-1621), his son; Earl of Hertford (1547); m. (in 1561) Catherine Grey, sister of Lady Jane.

Seymour, Thomas (1508?-49), brother of Jane Seymour; created

Baron Seymour of Sudeley and lord admiral (1547); m. (in 1547) Catherine Parr, widow of Henry VIII; beheaded by Edward VI.

Seymour, Jane (1509?-37); m. (in 1536) Henry VIII, his third wife; died following the birth of Edward VI.

Sidney, Henry (1529-86); raised at court as companion of Prince Edward; m. Mary Dudley, daughter of the Duke of Northumberland; father of Sir Philip Sidney, noted poet, statesman, and soldier.

Somerset, Duke of, *see* Seymour, Edward.

Southampton, Earl of, *see* Wriothesley, Thomas.

Stuart, Mary, *see* Mary, Queen of Scots.

Suffolk, Duke of, *see* (1) Brandon, Charles; (2) Grey, Henry.

Warwick, Earl of, *see* Dudley family.

Winchester, Bishop of, *see* Gardiner, Stephen.

Wriothesley, Thomas (1505-50); lord chancellor (1544); created Earl of Southampton (1547).

Wyatt (or Wyat), Thomas (1521?-54); led rebellion against Queen Mary; executed.

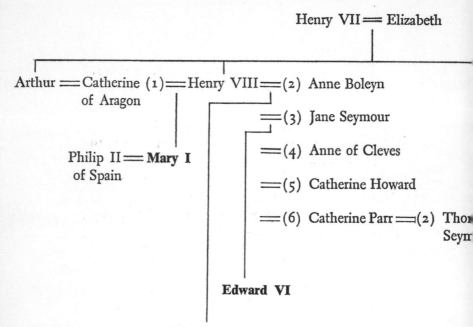

Henry VII ══ Elizabeth

Arthur ══ Catherine (1) ══ Henry VIII ══ (2) Anne Boleyn
of Aragon

══ (3) Jane Seymour

Philip II ══ **Mary I**   ══ (4) Anne of Cleves
of Spain

══ (5) Catherine Howard

══ (6) Catherine Parr ══ (2) Thor
Seyn

Edward VI

Elizabeth I

NOTE: The horizontal ══ marks indicate marriages. The vertical lines indicate children of a given marriage.

Margaret Tudor was older than Henry VIII, but it is clearer to make the chart in this way.